NATIONAL COLLEGE OF EDUCATION

TEST OF ADOLESCENT/ADULT WORD FINDING **TAWF**

Diane J. German, Ph.D.

ADMINISTRATION, SCORING AND INTERPRETATION MANUAL

Designed by Plunk Design

Printed in the U.S.A.

ISBN 1-55924-288-4

0 9 8 7 6 5 4 3 2 1 90 91 92 93 94 95 96

TABLE OF CONTENTS

LIST OF TABLES

LIST OF FIGURES

CHAPTER ONE

PURPOSE, STRUCTURE, AND CONTENT

The National College of Education *Test of Adolescent/Adult Word Finding* (TAWF) is a nationally standardized, individually administered, diagnostic tool for the assessment of word-finding skills in adolescent students and adults. Norms are provided for middle and secondary school students, 12 years 0 months to 19 years 11 months, in grades 7 through 12. Norms are also provided for adults, 20 years 0 months to 80 years 0 months. The TAWF consists of 107 items organized into five naming sections:

Section 1, *Picture Naming: Nouns*
Section 2, *Sentence Completion Naming*
Section 3, *Description Naming*
Section 4, *Picture Naming: Verbs*
Section 5, *Category Naming*

A special section is provided to assess knowledge of target words on the TAWF—Section 6, *Comprehension Assessment.* Word-finding skills are formally measured on two dimensions: accuracy of naming and speed of naming. In addition, a shortened version of the test, the TAWF Brief Test, is included for use with those individuals who may be unable to complete the entire TAWF due to test fatigue resulting from their particular disability. The TAWF Brief Test may also be administered in situations where time constraints make it impractical to administer the complete TAWF. The items on the TAWF Brief Test are presented in a separate section in the *Test Book* and marked on the *Response Booklet.* Chapter 5 of this manual discusses the TAWF Brief Test in depth.

This manual contains a description of the purpose, structure, and content of the TAWF and gives step-by-step procedures for test administration, scoring, and interpretation. A companion manual, the TAWF *Technical Manual,* contains an in-depth discussion of the theoretical basis, related research, development, and standardization of the TAWF, as well as evidence of its technical characteristics, reliability, and validity.

SCHOOL AND CLINICAL APPLICATIONS

Although the presence of word-finding problems in children has long been recognized (Johnson & Myklebust, 1967; Rutherford & Telser, 1967), it has only been in the last 12 years that this expressive language disorder in children has been the focus of research. Recent literature and empirical investigations have centered on the definition, characteristics, prevalence, assessment, and intervention of word-finding problems in children (Denckla & Rudel, 1976a, 1976b; Fried-Oken, 1984; German, 1979, 1983, 1984; Kail & Leonard, 1986; Leonard, Nippold, Kail, & Hale, 1983; Wiig & Semel, 1976, 1984; Wiig, Semel, & Nystrom, 1982; Wolf, 1980). To assess word-finding disorders in elementary-school-age children, a nationally standardized test, the *Test of Word Finding* (TWF) (German, [1986] 1989), was developed. This instrument was developed because of the strong need for a standardized test that would give professionals both systematic procedures for assessing word-finding skills in children and nationally representative norms on children's word finding. To respond to this same need in the diagnosis of word-finding disorders in the adolescent and adult populations, the National College of Education *Test of Adolescent/Adult Word Finding* (TAWF) was developed. The TAWF was designed to assist professionals in the assessment of an individual's word-finding skills by providing extensively researched naming tasks and systematic test procedures supported by reliability and validity investigations and representative normative data.

IDENTIFICATION

The TAWF is intended to assist speech and language pathologists, learning disability teachers, school psychologists, reading specialists, and other clinicians and special educators in assessing word-finding skills in middle and secondary school students and in adults. Prior to the development of the TWF (German, [1986] 1989) and the TAWF, professionals relied on informal assessment to determine word-finding difficulties. Although insightful, the results of such assessments often demonstrated poor reliability and were difficult to document and communicate to parents and other school personnel. In contrast, the TAWF provides the examiner with a formal, reliable assessment procedure for measuring a person's accuracy (standard scores and percentile ranks) and speed (response time) in naming. Because the TAWF allows the examiner to compare an individual's naming performance with that of normal people in a large standardization sample, the individual's word-finding skills can be reliably identified. In addition, the TAWF presents a procedure for analyzing the nature of naming responses and observing the presence of secondary characteristics (gestures and extra verbalizations) of naming behavior, resulting in a more precise identification of word-finding difficulties. In summary, the TAWF provides a structure for describing an individual's naming behavior to parents, other family members, teachers, and other school and medical personnel with respect to accuracy, speed, substitution types, and the presence of gestures and extra verbalizations.

PROGRAMMING

Intervention for word-finding disorders falls into three categories: remediation, compensatory programming, and self-awareness. Intervention effectiveness is based on the professional's understanding of the subject's word-finding skills. Although word-finding assessment should include information from many sources (diagnostic tests, home and classroom observations, etc.), information obtained from the TAWF enhances understanding of an individual's word-finding skills and thus aids in determining the most appropriate intervention program for those with word-finding difficulties.

A series of special TAWF features provide valuable programming information. Individuals with both accuracy and response-time difficulties need programming different from those manifesting either accuracy or response-time deficits alone. Therefore, comparisons of TAWF response time and accuracy can guide appropriate intervention techniques for a particular person. Second, the TAWF provides a model for analyzing substitution responses expressed by someone who is having difficulty finding a target word. Knowledge of the unique substitutions used by a particular person while manifesting word-finding difficulties can provide insights into the type of naming strategies employed. Thus the substitution analyses on the TAWF yield information important for individualizing remedial programs. Lastly, the TAWF provides a means of analyzing secondary characteristics of word-finding problems. An analysis of such secondary characteristics that accompany word-finding difficulties is helpful both to those subjects who must learn to inhibit such behaviors and to family members and professionals who need to recognize these behaviors to identify when specific individuals manifest difficulties in word finding. This multifaceted approach to the assessment of word-finding skills contributes to the development of a more comprehensive, individualized intervention program for the individual with word-finding problems.

REMEDIAL PROGRESS AND PROGRAM EVALUATION

Due to its psychometrically robust and technically sound diagnostic components, the TAWF can also be used in evaluating remedial progress. Follow-up testing at specific programming intervals can provide needed documentation of progress and can help determine if remedial programming has been effective. Specifically, through a pre- and posttest assessment sequence, the examiner can observe improvement in both naming speed and accuracy and note changes in naming strategies and reduction of secondary characteristics following a specific period of intervention. It could also be used to help assess recovery of aphasic patients or deterioration with aging or dementia.

RESEARCH

In addition to its diagnostic and programming applications in clinic and classroom settings, the TAWF is an excellent instrument for use in investigations of word-finding skills. The TAWF's standardized procedures and normative data allow the researcher to conduct reliable and valid comparative studies of word-finding skills. Because both the formal and informal measures of the TAWF consider variables identified through research as important in word-finding assessment, researchers can conduct comprehensive studies of subjects' word-finding abilities. For example, the TAWF may be employed in research on the prevalence and nature of word-finding deficits in various groups of adolescents as well as in studies of the relationship between word-finding skills and academic achievement. In particular, the incidence of word-finding difficulties in normally achieving adolescents and exceptional students could be determined. Using the TAWF, researchers may contrast the word-finding skills of normal achievers with those of stutterers, bilingual students, linguistically handicapped students with and without receptive language problems, and other exceptional individuals to arrive at important insights into the various manifestations of this expressive language disorder. Such experimental studies of word-finding disorders in the adolescent population should be especially helpful in determining the nature of this expressive language disorder when it continues from childhood into adolescence. The TAWF could also be used to help assess the difference between word recognition and retrieval skills in the aging population. For patients with reduced attention span because of various dementias (including Alzheimer's), the TAWF Brief Test might be used (see Chapter 5).

DIAGNOSTIC MODEL

The TAWF is based on a diagnostic model drawn from the literature on word finding in children and adults. The model considers those variables identified as influencing word-finding behavior during assessment and incorporates indices used to define word-finding problems in children and adults. Figure 1-1 displays the diagnostic model underlying the TAWF.

NAMING TASKS

Stimulus context refers to the nature of the naming task used to assess word-finding skills in constrained naming. Hierarchies of difficulty in stimulus context have been reported in the word-finding ability of adults (Barton, Maruszewski, & Urrea, 1969; Goodglass & Stuss, 1979) and children (German, 1984; Rudel, Denckla, Broman, & Hirsch, 1980). See the TAWF *Technical Manual* for a discussion of stimulus context. The TAWF considers naming in various stimulus contexts as it includes items that are representative of four different stimulus contexts: picture naming, naming to open-ended sentences, naming to description, and category naming. Specifically, the naming assessment in the TAWF consists of picture naming sections (nouns and verbs); a sentence completion naming section (nouns); a description naming section (nouns); and a category naming section (category words). Because items that represent multiple stimulus contexts are included in the total score, the TAWF provides a broader assessment of word-finding skills than the traditional picture-naming task only. In addition, although standard scores are not provided by section, a person's word-finding skills on the TAWF can be informally assessed by section.

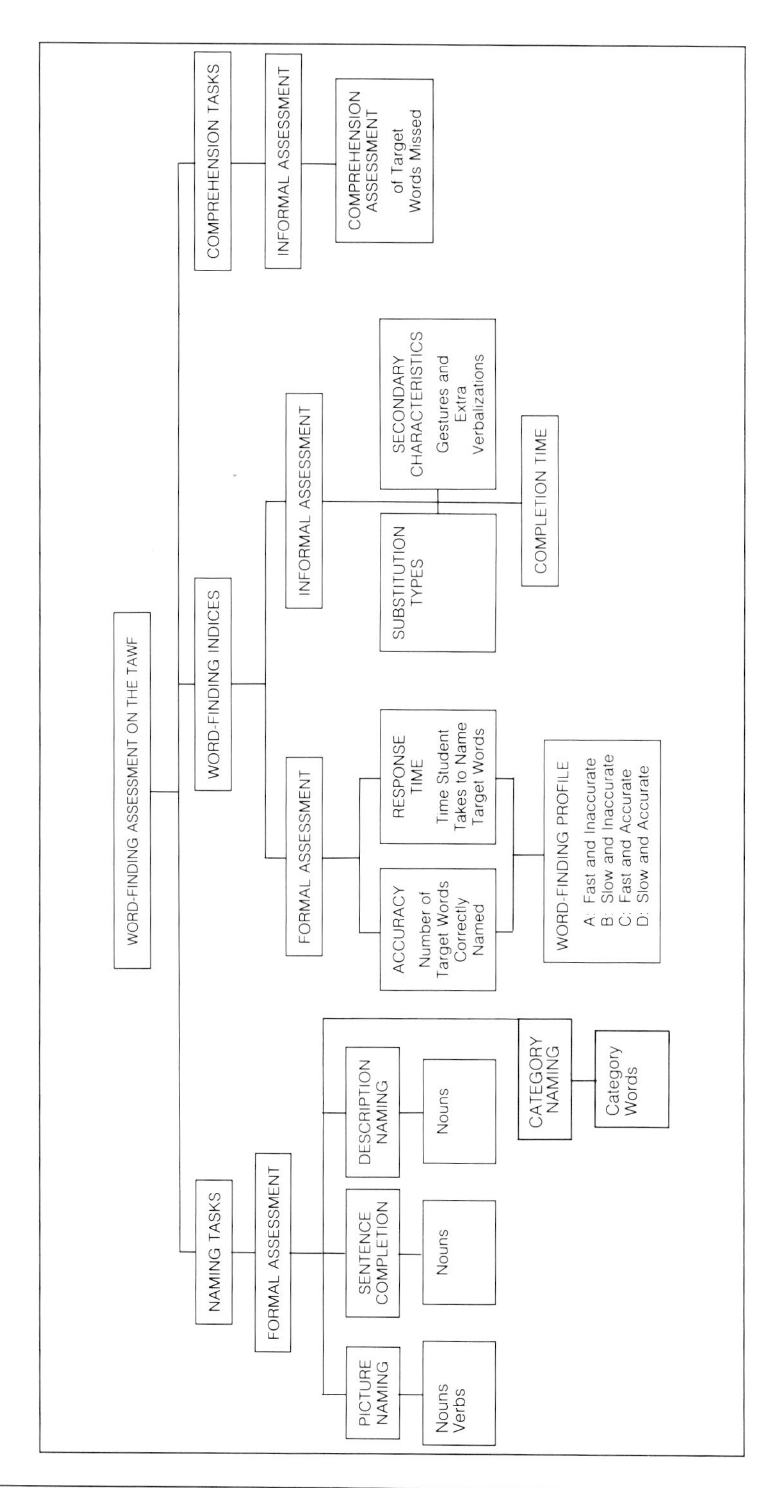

Figure 1-1. Diagnostic model for comprehensive assessment of word-finding skills using the National College of Education *Test of Adolescent/Adult Word Finding* (TAWF).

FORMAL ASSESSMENT OF WORD FINDING

Word-finding problems in children have been defined in the research literature according to one or any combination of the following three indices: accuracy score, response time, and substitution types (response analysis).

Accuracy

The TAWF's accuracy measurement is an index of the number of target words an individual is able to name correctly on the first response during assessment. In contrast to the response-time measurement, it provides insight into the selection process itself. Measuring accuracy allows for follow-up analyses of target-word substitutions which may aid in the identification of naming strategies employed by the person under study. The usefulness of an accuracy index in word-finding assessment has been verified in numerous studies (discussed further in the TAWF *Technical Manual*).

The accuracy score, the main index utilized in the TAWF, consists of a total raw score converted into derived scores—percentile ranks or standard scores—based on age or grade. This score enables the examiner to compare an individual's naming accuracy with grade and age mates in the standardization sample.

Response Time

The TAWF's response-time assessment measures the time a subject takes to find the target word or an approximation of the target word. This index has been used to assess word retrieval skills in adults and in children in many investigations (discussed further in the TAWF *Technical Manual*).

The TAWF provides two procedures for analyzing response latencies: (1) an Estimated Item Response Time procedure; and (2) an Actual Item Response Time measurement. For either procedure, measurement is based on the response time for each item administered in Section 1, Picture Naming: Nouns. The Estimated Item Response Time procedure classifies as a Slow Namer any individual exhibiting a number of response delays (of 4 seconds or longer) greater than a number established as the grade-level standard for his or her grade-/age-level peers in the standardization sample. The Actual Item Response Time measurement classifies as a Slow Namer any individual whose average item response time (total item response time divided by 37—the total number of items in Section 1 of the complete test) is longer than the grade-/age-level standards for his or her peers in the standardization sample. The Grade-Level Standards for both the Estimated Item Response Time and Actual Item Response Time procedures are reported in Appendix F.

INFORMAL ASSESSMENT OF WORD FINDING

The TAWF provides the examiner with an informal evaluation procedure for analyzing a subject's error responses (substitution analysis) and secondary characteristics on the various naming sections. These analyses are discussed in the following section.

Substitution Analysis

An analysis of the type of substitutions manifested by individuals having difficulty naming target words is useful for identifying people with word-finding problems. This analysis provides insights into semantic structure and semantic processing, as well as frequently indicating to the examiner the individual's general knowledge about a target word he or she is unable to name. Identification of response patterns has both diagnostic and remedial implications. Diagnostically, response patterns may aid in differentiating various types of expressive language disorders, while remedially they can provide guidelines for choosing appropriate cuing and organizing techniques. In addition, because different naming patterns have emerged in different studies, use of particular substitution types may be influenced by the nature of the naming task and may be specific to an individual's own lexical storage system. Error pattern analysis, then, is specific to the word-finding assessment used and the person under study. Substitution patterns have been identified in many studies of word-finding disorders. (An in-depth discussion of this research is presented in the TAWF *Technical Manual.*) The TAWF provides the examiner with an informal evaluation procedure for analyzing error responses on the various naming sections. This response analysis model was derived from psycholinguistic studies of the different semantic and lexical relationships between words (Evens, Litowitz, Markowitz, Smith, & Werner, 1983; Lyons, 1977; Riegel, 1970). In addition, it incorporates substitution types drawn from adult and child literature as well as response categories generated from the individuals with word-finding problems in the TAWF standardization sample.

Response categories for Sections 1, 2, 3, and 5 consist of the following general categories: semantic, perceptual, substitution plus self-correction, nonspecific words, circumlocutions, and no response. (See Chapter 4 for a discussion of the specific subcategories for each of these general groupings.) Response categories for Section 4 include the categories listed above, along with response categories that are unique to the Picture Naming: Verbs section—pro-verbal action responses, related noun responses, root-word verb responses, picture labeling, and innovative verb responses. (See Chapter 4 for descriptions and examples of each of these response categories.)

This informal analysis of substitution types follows the formal accuracy and time assessments discussed previously. It should be completed on those subjects who manifest word-finding problems on the TAWF. In most cases this would be a person whose accuracy score is one standard deviation or more below the mean of the normal subjects in the standardization sample and whose comprehension score indicates that the person knew the words he or she was unable to name. However, a substitution analysis might also be completed for a subject whose accuracy score is in the borderline range or whose overall comprehension score is low but who manifests word-finding difficulties on target words he or she knows. In this case, the substitution analysis should be considered on only those words the individual knew but could not name.

Secondary Characteristics

Secondary characteristics refer to those behaviors that often accompany efforts to verbalize target words in constrained or spontaneous naming situations. Two types of secondary characteristics—*gestures* (mime of the target word, tapping, pointing, or nonverbal indication of frustration, etc.) and *extra verbalizations* ("it's a," "oh," "I know it," etc.)—may be present when a person is manifesting word-finding difficulties.

In a study of the development of gestures in children, Barten (1979) identified five gesture types: deictic, instrumental, expressive, enactive, and depictive. Johnson and Myklebust (1967) clinically observed the use of these gesture types along with extra verbalizations when children with learning disabilities have difficulty retrieving words. According to these authors, younger children may resort to acoustic representations of the target word, while others may use gestures or pantomime to communicate their message. Wiig and Semel (1984) indicated that learning disabled children may produce "idiosyncratic hand movements," manifest "facial grimaces," "hit the table," "swing a leg," or "tap a rhythm with one foot" while struggling to find a word to express their thoughts (p. 112). Fried-Oken (1984) categorized these behaviors as error types, while labeling gestures as "nonverbal circumlocutions" and comments as "noninformative responses." Classifying the same behaviors as secondary characteristics of word-finding difficulties, German (1982, 1984) analyzed the frequency of occurrence of gestures and extra verbalizations in the naming behavior of language-impaired students with learning disabilities. Students with word-finding problems were found to engage in significantly more gestures and extra verbalizations on those naming tasks where they manifested more errors and longer response times than on naming tasks on which they performed similarly to their normally language-learning counterparts (German, 1985).

Extra verbalizations appear to aid in the search for target words as they often provide cues for naming (target word "funnel"; "It sounds like tunnel") as well as indications of knowledge of the target word ("Oh, I know it, but I can't think of it"). Gestural behavior appears to give nonverbal support to the word-finding process. In an attempt to name "jack," one student mimed the action for raising an automobile; another student mimed playing an instrument while trying to name "harmonica."

These findings emphasize the need to look beyond a subject's actual word-finding scores. To this end, the TAWF provides the examiner with an informal observation procedure for systematically noting the presence of secondary word-finding characteristics during naming tasks (see Chapter 2).

These observations of secondary characteristics in naming can play an important role in both compensatory programming and remediation for the individual with word-finding disorders. First, identification of those secondary characteristics that are specific to a particular person's naming behavior (use of gestures or extra verbalizations or both) should be communicated to family members and professionals to help them identify when an individual is having word-finding difficulties. The presence of either of these secondary characteristics should signal to the listener that a particular person is manifesting word-finding difficulties and the listener might then use compensatory techniques to aid the retrieval at that moment (provide multiple choices, the initial sound, or extended time to retrieve the target word). Second, remediation should focus on using the energy expended on those secondary characteristics, which may be distracting and nonconstructive, for naming strategies that will facilitate retrieval.

In conclusion, observing a person, as well as listening to the struggle to find words on the naming tasks may (a) clarify whether the individual knows the target word, thus indicating whether the noted naming difficulties are truly a problem in word finding; (b) provide evidence of the cues used during the naming process; and (c) give insights into the level of frustration experienced during the naming task. Such information can help ascertain the extent of language intervention necessary for the individual (German, 1985).

Comprehension Tasks

By definition, people with word-finding problems have difficulty naming target words in the presence of good comprehension of those words that they are unable to name (Johnson & Myklebust, 1967; Wiig & Semel, 1984). Therefore, the purpose of the comprehension assessment is to check the subject's knowledge of the target words he or she is unable to name or has named incorrectly. This type of information will aid the examiner in differentiating between receptive and expressive language difficulties on the TAWF.

COMPONENTS

The National College of Education *Test of Adolescent/Adult Word Finding* (TAWF) contains four components: the TAWF *Test Book,* the TAWF *Response Booklet,* the TAWF *Technical Manual,* and this manual, the TAWF *Administration, Scoring and Interpretation Manual.*

TAWF TEST BOOK

All TAWF stimulus items are presented in the TAWF *Test Book.* The test book is designed in an easel format to be set up with the pictures facing the subject and the examiner's directions facing the examiner. The test book is divided into five naming task sections and a section for assessing comprehension: (1) Picture Naming: Nouns; (2) Sentence Completion Naming; (3) Description Naming; (4) Picture Naming: Verbs; (5) Category Naming; and (6) Comprehension Assessment. A final section includes the TAWF Brief Test items.

TAWF RESPONSE BOOKLET

The 8-page individualized TAWF *Response Booklet* is designed to be used with the test book during administration of the TAWF (either complete test or Brief Test) and to record all test results. Formal test results are recorded and plotted in the summary sections of the front and back covers (pages 1 and 8). Pages 2 through 6 provide spaces to record subject responses for each item. Page 7 contains a special section for summarizing all informal assessment information.

TAWF TECHNICAL MANUAL

The companion TAWF *Technical Manual* provides an in-depth discussion of the theoretical foundations, research, development, and standardization of the TAWF, as well as reports of reliability, validity, and other technical characteristics of the TAWF.

TAWF ADMINISTRATION, SCORING AND INTERPRETATION MANUAL

This manual presents step-by-step procedures for administering, scoring, and interpreting the results of the TAWF. All norm tables are included in this administration manual. They should be used with the response booklet for converting raw scores to derived scores.

CONTENT OF THE TAWF

The TAWF is based on a diagnostic model of word-finding assessment drawn from child and adult literature on word-finding disorders. The variables considered in the development of the TAWF format and the word-finding items were those reported in many child and adult studies as influencing word-finding skills. Variables include situational context, stimulus context, target-word frequency, and nature of the target word (semantic categories, prototypicality, and syntax). These variables are discussed further in the TAWF *Technical Manual.*

TAWF scoring is based on a total score which is representative of combined section scores. TAWF items are organized into five sections of naming tasks and a special section for assessing comprehension (see Table 1-1). Since each section of items represents different naming variables, each naming section is described individually in the following. The TAWF *Technical Manual* describes the item-analysis procedures used to develop items in each naming section. The TAWF Brief Test can be administered in certain circumstances. It is described in Chapter 5 of this manual and uses the same components as the complete test.

PICTURE NAMING: NOUNS

Section 1, Picture Naming: Nouns is a picture-naming task used to assess accuracy (standard scores and percentile ranks) and speed (estimated and actual item response time) in naming target words presented in a picture format. Picture naming is a traditional format for assessing word-finding skills (Denckla & Rudel, 1976a, 1976b; German, 1979; Kaplan, Goodglass, & Weintraub, 1976; Oldfield & Wingfield, 1965). Originally, a total of 88 nouns (target words) were

1 Table 1-1
Content of the TAWF

Section	Number of Items		Type of Stimulus	Measurements
	Complete	Brief Test		
Section 1, Picture Naming: Nouns	37	14	pictures	• accuracy • item response time (actual or estimated)
Section 2, Sentence Completion Naming	16	6	open-ended sentences in auditory context (cloze procedure)	• accuracy
Section 3, Description Naming	12	4	sentence descriptions in auditory context (three-attribute descriptions of target words)	• accuracy
Section 4, Picture Naming: Verbs	21	8	pictures of actions	• accuracy
Section 5, Category Naming	21	8	auditory presentation of three subordinate or basic object-level words that imply a category target word	• accuracy
Section 6 Comprehension Assessment	Administer only erred items from Sections 1-5		picture of target word in four-picture strip (three decoys)	Informal Measurement—percent of comprehension to determine knowledge of target words missed

identified, drawn from four sources: the *Ginn Intermediate Dictionary* (Morris, 1974), the *Macmillan Dictionary for Children* (Halsey & Morris, 1977), and vocabulary lists from first- through sixth-grade *Ginn Basal Readers* (Johnson, Markert, Shuy, Squire, & Venezky, 1979) and first- through sixth-grade core and additional reading lists drawn from frequently used basal readers as presented by Harris and Jacobson (1972). Vocabulary was selected according to five variables identified through clinical observations and research as influencing word-finding skills: syntax, picturability, target-word frequency, syllabication, and semantic categories. Rigorous item analyses led to the final set of 37 target words in Section 1.

SENTENCE COMPLETION NAMING

Section 2, Sentence Completion Naming assesses accuracy (standard scores and percentile ranks) when naming words in an intrasensory auditory context in a cloze-procedure format. The unique nature of this naming task—a quality of automaticity leads the subject to the response—has made it useful for identifying students with word-finding problems (German, 1979, 1984) and reading disorders (Rudel, Denckla, & Broman, 1981), as well as adults with naming disorders (Barton et al., 1969). Initially, the sentence completion naming section consisted of 44 items. All items were declarative present tense sentences consisting of a minimum of two and a maximum of five associations to the target word. Sentences either defined the target word (definitional sentences = 62.5%) or contained vocabulary judged to be highly associated with the target word (associative sentences = 37.5%). Both sentence types provided naming clues judged to aid word finding (Tulving, 1974; Wiig & Semel, 1984). To aid subjects in the naming process, each of the definitional sentences provided salient characteristics of the target word such as function, location, or perceptual attributes, while each associative sentence included vocabulary that is frequently paired with the target word. The implied target words were drawn from four sources: the *Ginn Intermediate Dictionary* (Morris, 1974), the *Macmillan Dictionary for Children* (Halsey & Morris, 1977), and vocabulary lists from first- through sixth-grade *Ginn Basal Readers* (Johnson et al., 1979) and first- through sixth-grade core and additional reading lists drawn from frequently used basal readers as presented by Harris and Jacobson (1972). Vocabulary selected was structured according to syntax, target-word frequency, and syllabication. After rigorous item analyses, the final set of 16 open-ended sentences and target words was selected for Section 2.

DESCRIPTION NAMING

Section 3, Description Naming is designed to assess naming accuracy (standard scores and percentile ranks) in an intrasensory auditory synthesis task where the subject is required to name a target word implied by three attributes. As indicated earlier, naming tasks of this nature have been used to identify children with word-finding problems (German, 1979, 1984) and reading disorders (Rudel et al., 1981), as well as adults with naming disorders (Barton et al., 1969; Goodglass & Stuss, 1979; Luria, 1980). Initially, this section consisted of 46 items. All descriptions consisted of *wh*-questions defining the target word, using two to four salient attributes. Each description included the target-word category or function or both and one to three of the following features identified as the most salient attributes of the target word: composition, location, size, or sound. Definitions were drawn from the *Ginn Intermediate Dictionary* (Morris, 1974) and implied target words were drawn from four sources: the *Ginn Intermediate Dictionary,* the *Macmillan Dictionary for Children* (Halsey & Morris, 1977), and vocabulary lists from first- through sixth-grade *Ginn Basal Readers* (Johnson et al., 1979) and first- through sixth-grade core and additional reading lists drawn from frequently used basal readers as presented by Harris and Jacobson (1972). Vocabulary selection for this stimulus context was structured according to syntax, target-word frequency, and syllabication. Rigorous item analyses yielded the final 12 items in Section 3.

PICTURE NAMING: VERBS

Section 4, Picture Naming: Verbs is designed to assess accuracy (standard scores and percentile ranks) in naming action target words. Subjects are asked to label the action in a given picture. Naming actions presented in a picture format has been employed to assess word-finding skills in adults with aphasia (Goodglass, Klein, Carey, & Jones, 1966). Originally, this section consisted of 71 target verbs in the present participle form, drawn from four sources: the *Ginn Intermediate Dictionary* (Morris, 1974), the *Macmillan Dictionary for Children* (Halsey & Morris, 1977), and vocabulary lists from first- through sixth-grade *Ginn Basal Readers* (Johnson et al., 1979) and first- through sixth-grade core and additional reading lists drawn from frequently used basal readers as presented by Harris and Jacobson (1972). Vocabulary selection was structured according to four variables identified through clinical observations and research as influencing word-finding skills: syntax, picturability, target-word frequency, and syllabication. After rigorous item analyses, the final set of 21 target words and pictorial representations of actions was selected for Section 4.

CATEGORY NAMING

Section 5, Category Naming is designed to assess accuracy (standard scores and percentile ranks) in naming category words. Specifically, subjects are asked to name the implied category word for three subordinate or basic object-level words read by the examiner. Words representing objects at the basic object level have been identified experimentally as (a) having attributes in common, (b) sharing motor movements, and (c) exhibiting object similarity in shape (Rosch,

1977; Rosch, Mervis, Gray, Johnson, & Boyes-Braem, 1976). Basic object-level words are contrasted with superordinate terms (e.g., the difference between "trout" and "fish," "sparrow" and "bird," "chair" and "furniture"); basic objects have been shown to influence imagery, perception of categories, naming practices, and perhaps even language structure.

Research in adult aphasia has investigated aphasics' ability to name instances of superordinate terms and has recommended category-naming tasks to assess word-finding skills of adult aphasics in an effort to determine disturbances of the "nominative function at a high level" (Luria, 1980, p. 514). Initially, this stimulus context consisted of 60 target words, each word represented by three exemplars. Category target words and their category members were drawn from six sources: Rosch (1975) word lists of semantic categories and basic object-level members, Battig and Montague (1969) category norms for verbal items in 56 categories, the *Ginn Intermediate Dictionary* (Morris, 1974), the *Macmillan Dictionary for Children* (Halsey & Morris, 1977), and vocabulary lists from first- through sixth-grade *Ginn Basal Readers* (Johnson et al., 1979) and first- through sixth-grade core and additional reading lists drawn from frequently used basal readers as presented by Harris and Jacobson (1972). Vocabulary was selected according to variables identified as influencing word-finding skills by current research on prototypicality and by clinical observations and research. These variables include syntax, frequency, taxonomic level, and syllabication. Following rigorous item analyses, a final set of 21 category target words was selected for Section 5.

COMPREHENSION ASSESSMENT

Section 6, Comprehension Assessment provides a means of assessing subjects' comprehension of items named incorrectly in Sections 1 through 5. By definition, individuals with word-finding problems have difficulty naming target words in the presence of good comprehension of those words (Johnson & Myklebust, 1967; Wiig & Semel, 1984). Therefore, the purpose of the comprehension assessment is to check an individual's knowledge of those target words he or she is unable to name or has named incorrectly. The results will aid the examiner in differentiating between receptive and expressive language difficulties on the TAWF. Good target-word comprehension would be expected on erred items thought to represent word-finding problems. This evaluation is performed after the word-finding assessment is completed. The vocabulary for the comprehension evaluation consists of all the target words on the TAWF. Each target word is grouped with three decoys in a four-picture format. The items administered to assess a particular person's comprehension include only the target words missed in the TAWF naming sections. That is, only pictures containing the erred items are presented. Assessment of target-word comprehension does not require naming, but uses a recognition response only.

CHAPTER TWO

ADMINISTRATION PROCEDURES

GENERAL ADMINISTRATION PROCEDURES

The TAWF is a nationally standardized test and thus the standardized administration procedures presented in this chapter must be strictly adhered to in order to ensure valid results. The TAWF was designed to be an individually administered diagnostic tool for the assessment of word-finding skills. The TAWF was developed for students 12 years 0 months through 19 years 11 months in grades 7 through 12 and for adults aged 20 through 80 years.

TEST MATERIALS

The TAWF includes a test book, response booklets, an administration, scoring, and interpretation manual, and a technical manual. To administer the TAWF, the examiner will need the following:

The TAWF *Test Book*
A TAWF *Response Booklet*
This TAWF *Administration, Scoring and Interpretation Manual*
Pencil or marking pen

In addition, if the optional Actual Item Response Time measurement is to be used after the TAWF administration, the examiner will also need:

Audio cassette tape recorder
Blank audio cassette tape
Stopwatch with digital display that records to hundredths of a second

This procedure is also recommended for those examiners who wish to keep an audio record of the testing for later review or analysis.

TAWF Test Book

The TAWF *Test Book* contains the TAWF test items organized in the sequence in which they are to be presented. The test book includes seven tabbed sections: (1) Picture Naming: Nouns; (2) Sentence Completion Naming; (3) Description Naming; (4) Picture Naming: Verbs; (5) Category Naming; (6) Comprehension Assessment; and (7) TAWF Brief Test.

The test book, designed in an easel format, is to be set up with target-word pictures facing the subject and the test directions facing the examiner. The examiner should follow the directions presented on the examiner's side for each section. The TAWF does not have a basal or ceiling; all items are administered on the TAWF.

TAWF Response Booklet

The 8-page individualized TAWF *Response Booklet* is designed to be used with the test book during test administration of the TAWF and to record all test results. Formal test results are recorded in the summary and interpretation sections of the front and back covers (pages 1 and 8). Pages 2 through 6 provide spaces to record subject responses for each test item. Page 7 of the response booklet contains a special section for summarizing all informal assessment information.

Audio Cassette Recorder and Tape

The TAWF measures word-finding skills by accuracy and speed (response time). Response speed can be measured during the TAWF administration by using the Estimated Item Response Time procedure or after the test administration by using the optional Actual Item Response Time measurement (see the scoring procedures for Section 1 in Chapter 3). If the Estimated Item Response Time procedure is used, a tape recorder is *not* needed. The optional Actual Item Response Time measurement, however, requires an audio tape recording of Section 1, Picture Naming: Nouns. To conduct the optional Actual Item Response Time measurement, the examiner must tape-record the presentation of all test items administered in Section 1. An audio cassette tape recorder and a blank audio cassette should be set up and ready for recording prior to test administration.

Stopwatch

If the examiner chooses to complete the optional Actual Item Response Time measurement, the examiner must use a stopwatch that measures time to hundredths of a second. (A digital stopwatch facilitates recording actual item response times to the nearest hundredth of a second.)

EXAMINER QUALIFICATIONS

Although formal training specific to the National College of Education *Test of Adolescent/Adult Word Finding* (TAWF) is not required to prepare an examiner to administer the TAWF, the examiner should have knowledge and experience in test administration, scoring, and interpretation of psychoeducational diagnostic instruments. To prepare for administering the TAWF, the examiner should first read this TAWF *Administration, Scoring and Interpretation Manual* and the TAWF *Response Booklet.* Second, in order to become completely familiar with this instrument and to facilitate smooth test administration, the examiner should complete *five trial administrations* of the TAWF before attempting to administer it to an individual under study.

TESTING ENVIRONMENT

The testing site should be conducive to valid, individualized assessment. Specifically, testing should take place in a well-lighted room, free of visual, auditory, or other distractions that could influence the subject's performance or interfere with the optional audio recording of Section 1, Picture Naming: Nouns, if employed. Seating arrangements should facilitate the examiner's manipulation of test materials and simultaneous recording of responses.

The subject and examiner should be seated across from one another as illustrated in Figure 2-1. The easel-format test book should be placed with the pictorial stimulus facing the subject and the word stimulus facing the examiner. Testing materials should be positioned so that the examiner can present the pictures with one hand while recording the responses with the other. Therefore, the response booklet should be situated conveniently near the examiner's dominant hand and out of the subject's obvious range of vision, with a marking pen nearby. If used, the tape recorder should be positioned midway between the subject and the examiner in order to record both the examiner's verbalization of the word NOW and the subject's naming response.

TIME REQUIREMENTS

The TAWF takes approximately 20 to 30 minutes to administer. Sufficient time should be scheduled so that the entire TAWF can be administered in one session. Picture presentation must be smooth, continuous, and uninterrupted.

Figure 2-1. Seating arrangement and organization of materials for TAWF administration.

To achieve a valid presentation, the examiner should present each pictorial stimulus immediately following the subject's response without any delay during or between page presentations. It is recommended that the examiner conduct five practice administrations before the actual test administration. The examiner should concentrate on flipping the pages of the easel test book with no delay between page presentations to develop a smooth, continuous style of presenting the TAWF test items.

GENERAL ORDER OF PRESENTATION

The TAWF test sections should be presented in the order indicated in the test book. This presentation order is also followed in the response booklet. The examiner should begin the administration of the TAWF with Section 1, Picture Naming: Nouns, and finish the naming portion of the TAWF with Section 5, Category Naming. After administering and recording the results for Sections 1 through 5, the examiner should administer Section 6, Comprehension Assessment. All naming errors on the TAWF should be checked for item comprehension to determine if the subject knows the target words and understands the stimulus sentences and descriptions. To administer the Comprehension Assessment, the examiner turns the response booklet back to page 2 for Section 1 and moves through each naming section, administering only those comprehension items that correspond to the incorrect responses in each section. The examiner simply checks "yes" or "no" (for pass or fail) for each comprehension item. It is not necessary to check comprehension of target words named correctly, as the subject has already indicated that he or she knows these words.

Within each section, items should be presented in the order indicated. The examiner should give the example items and the starter items before administering the test items. The example items help acquaint the subject with how to respond to each test item. Starter items in each section are designed to assist the examiner and the subject in establishing naming fluency and momentum for the actual test items. Both the examples and the starter items also serve to ease anxiety by providing practice in naming. **Do not score the examples or starter items.**

TAWF BRIEF TEST

The TAWF Brief Test consists of a selection of items from the complete TAWF. Chapter 5 of this manual describes the TAWF Brief Test. The general guidelines and section directions that follow are also appropriate for the Brief Test except as noted in Chapter 5.

GENERAL GUIDELINES

Specific administration procedures for each of the TAWF sections are presented later. However, some general administration guidelines are presented here to ensure a smooth administration of the TAWF.

ACCURACY ASSESSMENT

1. Simultaneously present the items and record the subject's responses. Always record and score the **first** response that is verbalized for the test item. (In word-finding assessment one always scores the first response, in contrast to receptive language assessment where one would score the last response.) The documentation of the incorrect responses will be used in subsequent analyses of the substitution types.
2. In preparation for scoring accuracy on the TAWF, mark correct responses with a "1" and record all incorrect responses (not the target word) in the response booklet. (See administration procedures for each section later in this chapter.) Incorrect responses are marked with a "0" after the error has been recorded. Even if a correct response is judged as delayed, it receives a score of "1" for accuracy. Recording incorrect responses while maintaining fluent presentation of the picture stimuli does require good administration skill. However, with practice, facility with this procedure can be obtained. As indicated previously, it is particularly important that fluent administration be maintained while recording responses in order to ensure a valid assessment.
3. When administering the TAWF test items, be careful not to give the correct answer or any kind of clue such as a gesture or beginning sound. Present each item immediately after the subject gives his or her response to the previous item. If a subject does not respond immediately, allow a maximum of 15 seconds before presenting the next item.

RESPONSE TIME ASSESSMENT

4. **The examiner may complete either the Estimated Item Response Time procedure or the Actual Item Response Time measurement. The examiner need complete only one of these response time procedures.** The examiner will gain facility with these procedures with five practice trials. Using an audio tape, an examiner can complete practice trials on the same subject's tape five times.
5. The Estimated Item Response Time procedure is completed during the TAWF administration of Section 1, Picture Naming: Nouns. In this procedure the examiner judges whether a given response time is more or less than 4 seconds. The student's naming speed is expressed as the total number of response delays (4 seconds or longer). This sum should be compared to the

number of delayed responses (4 seconds or longer) of the person's grade- or age-level peers in the standardization sample (see Appendix F).

6. **The Actual Item Response Time measurement is not completed during the administration of the TAWF.** (See scoring procedures for Section 1 in Chapter 3.) The Actual Item Response Time measurement is taken from the audio tape recording of Section 1, Picture Naming: Nouns, and is completed after the subject has left the testing room. To conduct the optional Actual Item Response Time measurement, the examiner must tape-record the presentation of all test items in Section 1 and verbalize the word NOW as each item in Section 1 is presented. The item response time measurement is the time between the examiner's verbalization of the word NOW (indicates presentation of the picture card) and the subject's response. The examiner measures the response time for each item, whether correct or incorrect, to the nearest hundredth of a second and records it in the response booklet adjacent to each item. An *Average Item Response Time* is then computed to assess a subject's speed in naming.
7. In the accuracy assessment, a "No Response" is scored as incorrect and assigned a score of 0. In the Estimated Item Response Time procedure any item where a subject does not make a response is judged to be a delayed response; i.e., a response time greater than 4 seconds. In the Actual Item Response Time measurement, a "No Response" item is assigned 15 seconds as the item response time.

SUBSTITUTION ANALYSIS

8. The informal analysis of the type of responses that a subject manifests when he or she is having difficulty naming a target word is completed after the TAWF has been administered (see Chapter 4 in this manual). The responses, recorded by the examiner during the administration of the TAWF, serve as the bases for this analysis.

SECONDARY CHARACTERISTICS

9. The presence of gestures or extra verbalizations (secondary characteristics) when a subject is having difficulty naming a target word is noted during the administration of the TAWF. (See scoring procedures for each section in Chapter 3.) The examiner simply checks the square in the appropriate column in the response booklet across from the target word on which the subject manifested gestures or produced extra verbalizations. It is not necessary to record the extra verbalizations verbatim or write the word *gestures*. A check mark in the gesture and extra verbalization columns in the space adjacent the appropriate target word is all that is necessary. The scores will be summarized and totaled after the administration session is completed.

The following presents detailed instructions for administering each section of the TAWF. The procedures should be studied thoroughly and practiced prior to actual test administration.

SPECIFIC ADMINISTRATION PROCEDURES

SECTION 1, PICTURE NAMING: NOUNS

This section was designed to assess an individual's speed and accuracy when naming picture referents of noun target words. It consists of 2 example pictures, 4 starter pictures, and 37 test pictures representing one- to four-syllable target words of different semantic categories. The pictures are black-and-white drawings with a color representation of the target word. The subject is asked to label the colored area of the presented picture. If the entire picture is colored, the subject is asked to name the whole picture. (See Figure 2-2 for a sample test item from Section 1.)

Following are the starter words and target words for Section 1 listed in order of presentation in the TAWF *Response Booklet.*

Examples	Starter Items	Test Items	
A. leaves	A. nose	1. ruler	20. film
B. trees	B. thumb	2. mask	21. backpack
	C. kite	3. antenna	22. unicorn
	D. whistle	4. statue	23. harmonica
		5. crutch	24. wishbone
		6. suspenders	25. propeller
		7. calculator	26. jack
		8. palm	27. thimble
		9. microphone	28. compass
		10. dice	29. funnel
		11. chopsticks	30. pliers
		12. battery	31. dustpan
		13. eyebrow	32. hopscotch
		14. binoculars	33. blimp
		15. dart	34. thermos
		16. magnet	35. tambourine
		17. acorn	36. spatula
		18. igloo	37. seahorse
		19. starfish	

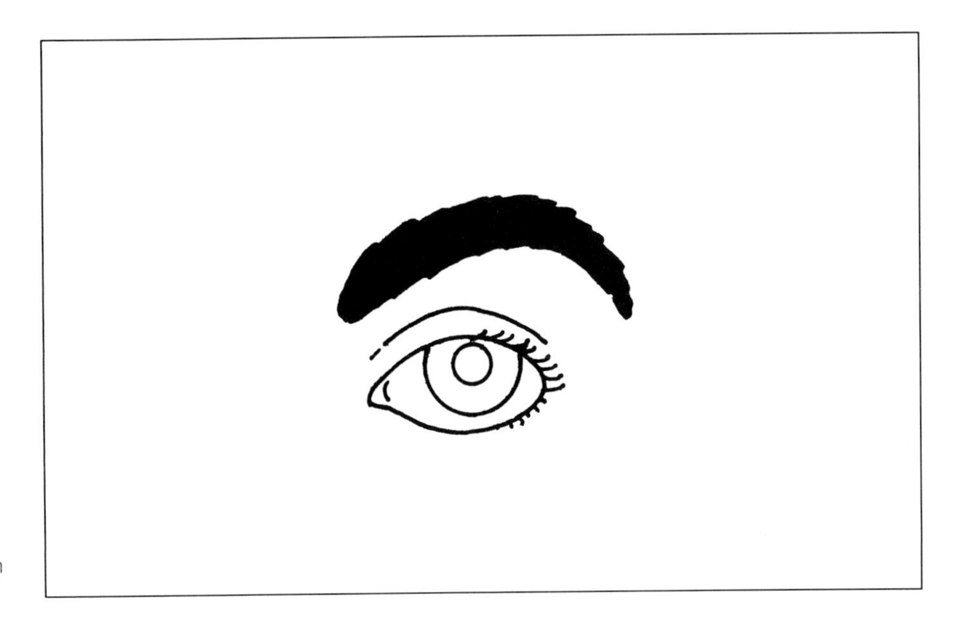

Figure 2-2. Sample test item from Section 1 (eyebrow).

Directions

Although the directions are clearly presented in the TAWF *Test Book,* they are repeated here with additional information to facilitate proper test administration. Read the following directions to the subject:

I will show you two types of pictures. Some pictures will have one part colored in and other pictures will be all colored. If the picture has only one part colored in, I want you to tell me the name of the colored part of the picture. If the whole picture is colored, then name the whole picture. There is only one word for each answer, so remember to give me only one word in your answer. Now look at this picture.

Examples

Show the subject example A (leaves) and say:

You would name this picture "leaves" because it is the only part of the picture that is colored. You would not say "tree" because the whole picture is not colored. What would you *name this picture?*

If the subject says "leaves," continue to example B (tree). If not, name the picture a second time and proceed to example B.

Now you would name this picture "tree" because the whole picture is colored. What would you *name this picture?*

If the subject says "tree," say, *Yes, tree is correct.* Then present the starter items. If the subject does not say "tree," name the picture a second time, then present the starter items.

Starter Items

Since the starter items are not test items, they are not included in the accuracy and time evaluations. As a result, starter items may be used if needed to teach the task to the subject. Beginning with item A, present the four starter items. Remind the subject of the directions: *Remember to give only one word in your answer and name the part of the picture that is colored when I say "now."* Only if needed, remind the subject to name the part of the picture that is colored and to give only one-word answers. Following the starter items, continue with the TAWF test items.

Test Items

Proceed with the testing. If you are using the Estimated Item Response Time procedure for measuring speed in naming, begin to count silently a 4-second interval as soon as you say "now." If you are going to use the optional Actual Item Response Time measurement, turn on the tape recorder. As you present each picture, verbalize the word NOW. This will indicate the picture exposure on the tape recorder (Actual Item Response Time measurement). Again, be sure to say "now" as you present each picture so you can measure the time between the picture presentation and the subject's response when you listen to the audio tape. Picture presentation should be fluent, with each picture exposed immediately after the subject's response. If a subject fails to respond or says "I don't know," allow 15 seconds for the subject to respond before moving to the next item. Observe the 15-second time limit by noting the time on your watch or stopwatch when the item is presented plus 15 seconds. When that time is reached, proceed to the next item. If the subject responds within the 15-second time limit, go on to the next item. Stop the tape recorder after completion of Section 1.

Taping

The examiner has the option of completing the Estimated Item Response Time procedure or the Actual Item Response Time measurement. If the examiner decides to complete the latter, Section 1 must be tape-recorded. The examiner should start recording before presenting the first test item and stop taping after the subject responds to the last test item in Section 1.

Marking Responses

Accuracy. With the response booklet open to Section 1, Picture Naming: Nouns, mark a "1" for all correct responses adjacent the test item. For all incorrect responses, record the subject's complete response in the space provided and record a "0" adjacent the test item for which there was an error.

Estimated Item Response Time Procedure. The Estimated Item Response Time procedure is used to judge the amount of time it takes a subject to name a target word in Section 1, Picture Naming: Nouns. It is determined by judging whether the period between the presentation of each stimulus picture and the subject's first effort to name the target word is longer or shorter than 4 seconds. Judgment of a subject's response speed is completed during the TAWF administration. The examiner silently counts a 4-second interval as soon as the word NOW is verbalized and then judges whether the subject responded before or after the 4 seconds elapsed. The examiner then checks the column adjacent the target item that indicates whether the estimated item response time was greater or less than the 4-second cutoff.

Gestures. Gestures that indicate frustration with the naming task (snapping fingers, tapping, facial grimaces, etc.) or mime the target word (putting hands to eyes for binoculars or holding up thumb for thimble), occurring while the subject attempts to find a target word, should be noted with one check (√) per test item in the *Gesture* column.

Extra Verbalizations. Any additional verbalizations ("um, oh, I forgot it," "I know it, but I can't think of it," etc.) made during the naming process should be noted with one check (√) for each item on which this occurs in the *Extra Verbal* column.

All other spaces and columns in the response booklet are to be completed after the test administration. In summary, during administration of Section 1, record responses in four of the areas on page 2 of the response booklet: *1 or 0, Subject's Response, Gesture,* and *Extra Verbal.* If the Estimated Item Response Time procedure is completed, the examiner would record responses in the appropriate column for this index. (See Figure 2-3 for a sample of response recording for Section 1, Picture Naming: Nouns.)

SECTION 2, SENTENCE COMPLETION NAMING

This section was designed to assess an individual's accuracy when naming target words in an intrasensory, auditory, cloze-procedure format. It consists of 2 examples, 4 starter items, and 16 test items (open-ended sentences). All are declarative present tense sentences with a minimum of two and a maximum of five associations to the target word. The subject is asked to complete the sentence stated by the examiner by naming the target word that would best complete the sentence. Following are the examples, starter items, and test items for Section 2. Test items are listed in the order presented in the test book and the response booklet. (See Figure 2-4 for sample test items from Section 2.)

Section 1
Picture Naming: Nouns

Starter Items

A. nose	B. thumb	C. kite	D. whistle

Item	1 or 0		Subject's Response	Item Response Time			Ges. (✓)	Ex. Ver. (✓)	Comprehension Yes (✓) No		Response Code (after testing)
				X Estimated During Testing		☐ Actual from Tape Recording (sec/hun) (after testing)					
	Brief Test	Complete Test		Less Than 4 sec. (✓)	More Than 4 sec. (✓)				Yes	No	
1. ruler		1		✓		/					
2. mask		1			✓	/					
3. antenna		1		✓		/					
4. statue		0	man on a horse		✓	/					
5. crutch		1		✓		/					
6. suspenders		1		✓		/					
7. calculator		0	computer	✓		/					
8. palm		1		✓		/					
9. microphone		1		✓		/					
10. dice		1		✓		/					
11. chopsticks		1		✓		/					
12. battery		0	box		✓	/					
13. eyebrow		1		✓		/					
14. binoculars		1			✓	/	✓				
15. dart		1		✓		/					
16. magnet		1		✓		/					
17. acorn		0	fruit		✓	/					
18. igloo		1		✓		/					
19. starfish		0	shellfish	✓		/					
20. film		0	tape	✓		/					
21. backpack		1		✓		/					
22. unicorn		1		✓		/					
23. harmonica		1		✓		/					
24. wishbone		0	I don't know		✓	/					
25. propeller		1		✓		/					
26. jack		0	lifter		✓	/	✓				
27. thimble		1		✓		/					
28. compass		0	directions	✓		/					
29. funnel		0	siphon		✓	/					
30. pliers		0	wrench	✓		/					
31. dustpan		1		✓		/					
32. hopscotch		1		✓		/					
33. blimp		1			✓	/					
34. thermos		0	coffee cup	✓		/	✓				
35. tambourine		0	drum	✓		/					
36. spatula		1		✓		/	✓				
37. seahorse		0	dragon fish		✓	/					

Brief Test Raw Score	RAW SCORE	Total Delayed Items	Total Item Response Time	Ges. Total	Ex. Ver. Total	Comprehension Total
	23	10	/	4	0	(total unknown)

2

Figure 2-3. Sample of response recording for Section 1, Picture Naming: Nouns.

10. To grow a vegetable in a garden, you plant a ________. **seed**

11. The highest point of a mountain is the ________. **peak**

12. A round model of the earth is a ________. **globe**

Figure 2-4. Sample test items from Section 2, Sentence Completion Naming.

Examples

Example A: To unlock a door, you need to use a ______ (key).
Example B: At night you sleep in a ______ (bed).

Starter Items

Starter Item A: A bird lays eggs in a ______ (nest).
Starter Item B: An instructor of a football team is the football ______ (coach).
Starter Item C: The outer part of an apple pie is the pie • ______ (crust).
Starter Item D: The net-like structure that a spider weaves is a spider ______ (web).

Test Items

1. When you ride a horse, you sit on a leather ______ (saddle).
2. Hot melted rock flowing from an active volcano is called ______ (lava).
3. The officer showed his sheriff's ______ (badge).
4. A scientist looks at small things through a ______ (microscope).
5. You walk a dog with a leather ______ (leash).
6. The library book is kept on the book • ______ (shelf).
7. It's fun to shake a friendly dog's front ______ (paw).
8. A paper that indicates that you completed high school is your high school ______ (diploma).
9. When you hold a rose, you can prick your finger on a ______ (thorn).

10. To grow a vegetable in a garden, you plant a ______ (seed).
11. The highest point of a mountain is the ______ (peak).
12. A round model of the earth is a ______ (globe).
13. A person who rides racehorses is called a ______ (jockey).
14. To study the stars you look through a ______ (telescope).
15. A gentle song used to put babies to sleep is a ______ (lullaby).
16. The space between rows of seats is the ______ (aisle).

Directions

Read the following directions to the subject:

I will read a sentence to you. The last word of the sentence will be left out. I want you to tell me the word that best fits in that place. There is only one word for each answer, so remember to give me only one word in your answer.

Examples

Begin by reading example A. If the subject responds correctly, proceed to example B. If the subject responds incorrectly because he or she does not understand the task (for example, responds with two words), give the subject the target word and proceed to example B. If the subject fails example B, give the subject the target word and present the starter items.

Starter Items

Since the starter items are not test items, they are not included in the accuracy evaluation. As a result, they may be used if needed to teach the task to the subject. Begin with starter item A. Present the four starter items (nest, coach, crust, and web). Following the starter items, continue with the test items. Remind the subject: *Remember to give only one word in your answer.*

Test Items

Proceed with the testing. Sentence presentation should be fluent, and each sentence should be presented immediately following the subject's response. Sentences can be repeated if requested by the subject, or if the examiner feels the subject was not attending. When considering whether or not to repeat an item, the examiner should decide to repeat only if the subject has not yet responded. Sentences should not be repeated because the subject made a naming error. If a subject fails to respond in 15 seconds, proceed to the next item.

Marking Responses

Accuracy. With the response booklet open to Section 2, Sentence Completion Naming, mark a "1" for all correct responses adjacent the test item. For all incorrect responses, record the subject's complete response in the space provided and record a "0" adjacent the test item in which there was an error.

Gestures. Gestures that indicate frustration with the naming task (snapping fingers, tapping, facial grimaces, etc.) or mime the target word (putting hands on seat for saddle or touching finger tips for thorn, etc.), occurring while the subject attempts to find a target word, should be noted with one check (√) per test item in the *Gesture* column.

Extra Verbalizations. Any additional verbalizations ("um, oh, I forgot it," "I know it, but I can't think of it," etc.) made during the naming process should be noted with one check (√) for each item in the *Extra Verbal* column.

All other spaces and columns in the response booklet are to be completed after the test administration. In summary, during administration of Section 2, record responses in four of the columns on page 3 of the response booklet: *1 or 0, Subject's Response, Gesture,* and *Extra Verbal.*

SECTION 3, DESCRIPTION NAMING

This section was designed to assess an individual's accuracy when naming words in an intrasensory auditory task where the subject is required to name a target word implied by a description given by the examiner. Each description includes either or both the semantic category of the target word and a functional attribute and one to three of the following attributes of the implied target word: composition, location, size, and sound. This section consists of 2 examples, 4 starter items, and 12 test items. (See Figure 2-5 for sample test items from Section 3.)

Examples

Example A: What is used to open a door, is made of metal, and is put into a lock? (key)

Example B: What do you sleep in, has a mattress and a pillow, and is in your room? (bed)

Starter Items

Starter Item A: What is used for a bird's home, is made of small pieces of grass, and is found in a tree? (nest)

Starter Item B: What do you find at the beach, is soft to walk on, and is used to build play castles? (sand)

Starter Item C: What part of your face is used for eating, has teeth and a tongue, and is below your nose? (mouth)

Starter Item D: What do you put on an envelope, is rectangular or square, and has glue on the back? (stamp)

4. What is a moving stairway that is found in a department store and that takes people up and down? **escalator**

5. What is the name of a group of people chosen in court to hear evidence and give a verdict in a trial? **jury**

6. What is a machine that may be shaped like a person and is programmed to do certain human jobs? **robot**

Figure 2-5. Sample test items from Section 3, Description Naming.

Test Items

1. What gives people a warning, is used on police cars and fire trucks, and makes a loud noise? (siren)
2. What is a hat that is made of a hard material and is used to protect the head when playing football? (helmet)
3. What is a permanent picture that is drawn on your skin by putting color in with a needle? (tattoo)
4. What is a moving stairway that is found in a department store and that takes people up and down? (escalator)
5. What is the name of a group of people chosen in court to hear evidence and give a verdict in a trial? (jury)
6. What is a machine that may be shaped like a person and is programmed to do certain human jobs? (robot)
7. What do you plant in the ground that is small and hard and that grows into a flower or vegetable? (seed)
8. What is the kind of clothing that is funny or strange and is worn on stage or for a special party? (costume)

9. What is the imaginary circle around the earth halfway between the North and South Poles? (equator)
10. What is a large covered basket often found in your bedroom or bathroom in which you put dirty clothes? (hamper)
11. What is the name of the hair that is cut short and brushed down over the forehead? (bangs)
12. What is a long paddle made of wood that is used to move a boat through the water? (oar)

Directions

Read the following directions to the subject:

I will read a sentence to you. Each sentence will describe something, and I want you to tell me the name of what I am describing. There is only one word for each sentence, so remember to give me only one word in your answer.

Examples

Begin by reading example A. If the subject responds correctly, proceed to example B. If the subject responds incorrectly because he or she does not understand the task (for example, responds with two words), give the subject the target word and proceed to example B. If the subject fails example B, give the subject the target word and present the starter items.

Starter Items

Since the starter items are not test items, they are not included in the accuracy evaluation. As a result, they may be used if needed to teach the task to the subject. Beginning with starter item A, present the four starter items (nest, sand, mouth, and stamp). Following the starter items, continue with the test items. Remind the subject: *Remember to give only one word in your answer.*

Test Items

Proceed with the testing. Description presentation should be fluent and each description should be presented immediately following the subject's response. Descriptions can be repeated if requested by the subject, or if the examiner feels the subject was not attending. When considering whether or not to repeat the item, the examiner should decide to repeat only if the subject has not yet responded. Descriptions should not be repeated because the subject made a naming error. If the subject fails to respond in 15 seconds, proceed to the next item.

Marking Responses

Accuracy. With the response booklet open to Section 3, Description Naming, mark a "1" for all correct responses adjacent the test item. For all incorrect responses, record the subject's complete response in the space provided and record a "0" adjacent the test item in which there was an error.

Gestures. Gestures that indicate frustration with the naming task (snapping fingers, tapping, facial grimaces, etc.) or mime the target word (putting hands to head for helmet or to forehead for bangs, etc.), occurring while the subject attempts to find a target word, should be noted with one check (√) per test item in the *Gesture* column.

Extra Verbalizations. Any additional verbalizations ("um, oh, I forgot it," "I know it, but I can't think of it," etc.) made during the naming process should be noted with one check (√) for each item in the *Extra Verbal* column.

All other spaces and columns in the response booklet are to be completed after the test administration. In summary, during administration of Section 3, record responses in four of the columns on page 4 of the response booklet: *1 or 0, Subject's Response, Gesture,* and *Extra Verbal.*

SECTION 4, PICTURE NAMING: VERBS

This section was designed to assess an individual's accuracy in naming action words. Specifically, the subject is shown pictorial representations of 21 verbs (e.g., licking, winking) and asked to label the action in the picture. The section consists of 2 example pictures, 4 starter pictures, and 21 test pictures made up of two- to four-syllable target words that represent verbs in the present participle form (e.g., dripping). The subject is asked to tell what the person or object in the picture is doing. Following are the examples, starter items, and target words for Section 4. (Figure 2-6 displays a sample test item from Section 4.)

Examples	Starter Items	Test Items	
A. blowing	A. knocking	1. dancing	12. plugging
B. writing	B. catching	2. licking	13. filing
	C. diving	3. pulling	14. weighing
	D. packing	4. squeezing	15. grating
		5. dripping	16. begging
		6. rolling	17. threading
		7. drilling	18. knitting
		8. measuring	19. parachuting
		9. marching	20. directing
		10. braiding	21. developing
		11. winking	

Figure 2-6. Sample test item from Section 4, Picture Naming: Verbs (pulling).

Directions

Read the following directions to the subject:

I will show you some pictures and I want you to tell me one word that describes what the person in the picture is doing. Remember, say only one word for each picture.

Examples

Show the subject example A and ask, *What is she doing?* If the subject responds "blowing," present example B. If the subject responds "blowing out her candles," ask the subject to give a one-word answer only. If for the second response the subject responds "blowing," proceed to example B. If the subject does not respond correctly, say *blowing* and proceed to the next example and say, *What is he doing?* If the subject responds correctly to example B, continue to the starter items. If the subject does not respond correctly, give the correct answer for example B, *writing,* and continue to the starter items. Use the carrier phrase *What is he (or she) doing?* when presenting the examples and starter items. Do not use the carrier phrase when presenting the test items unless necessary to elicit a response.

Starter Items

Since the starter items are not test items, they are not included in the accuracy evaluation. As a result, they may be used if needed to teach the task to the subject. Beginning with starter item A, present the four starter items (knocking, catching, diving, and packing). Use the carrier phrase *What is he (or she) doing?* with each starter item. Remind the subject: *Remember to give only one word in your answer.* Correct any errors made on the starter items. Following the starter items, continue with the test items. Use the carrier phrase *What is he (or she) doing?* when presenting the examples and starter items. Do not use the carrier phrase when presenting the test items unless necessary to elicit a response.

Test Items

Proceed with the test items. Present all the verb pictures. Do not use the carrier phrase during the testing unless a subject begins to label aspects of the picture rather than the action. In such situations, remind the subject of the task, using the carrier phrase *What is he (or she) doing?* Picture presentation should be fluent, and each exposure should be made immediately following the subject's response. If a subject fails to respond in 15 seconds, move to the next item.

Marking Responses

Accuracy. With the response booklet open to Section 4, Picture Naming: Verbs, mark a "1" for all correct responses adjacent the test item. For all incorrect responses, record the subject's complete response in the space provided and record a "0" adjacent the test item in which there was an error.

Gestures. Gestures that indicate frustration with the naming task (snapping fingers, tapping, facial grimaces, etc.) or mime the target word (closing one eye for winking or moving feet for marching, etc.), occurring while the subject attempts to find a target word, should be noted with one check (√) per test item in the *Gesture* column.

Extra Verbalizations. Any additional verbalizations ("um, oh, I forgot it," "I know it, but I can't think of it," etc.) made during the naming process should be noted with one check (√) for each item in the *Extra Verbal* column.

All other spaces and columns in the response booklet are to be completed after the test administration. In summary, during administration of Section 4, record responses in four of the columns on page 5 of the response booklet: *1 or 0, Subject's Response, Gesture,* and *Extra Verbal.*

SECTION 5, CATEGORY NAMING

This section was designed to assess an individual's accuracy in naming category words. The section consists of 2 examples, 4 starter items, and 21 test pictures, each representing three subordinate or basic-level words (north, south, east) that imply a target word that names a category (directions). The subject is asked to name the category word for the three subordinate or basic-level words presented by the examiner. The examples, starter items, and test items are listed below. (See Figure 2-7 for sample test items from Section 5.)

Examples	Starter Items	Test Items	
A. numbers	A. birds	1. holidays	12. directions
B. money	B. candy	2. states	13. countries
	C. days	3. time	14. senses
	D. music	4. presidents	15. cities
		5. oceans	16. transportation
		6. rivers	17. metals
		7. planets	18. appliances
		8. dances	19. awards
		9. religions	20. organs
		10. seasons	21. punctuation
		11. silverware	

Directions

Read the following directions to the subject:

I will read three words and I want you to tell me one word that names the three words that I read you. Do not repeat the words that I say, but tell me a new word that names all three of the words that I say.

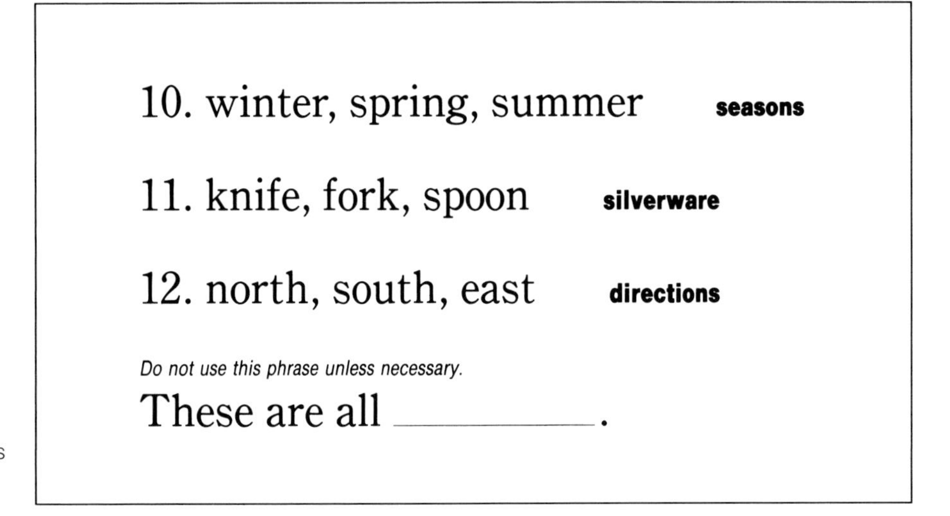

Figure 2-7. Sample test items from Section 5, Category Naming.

Examples

Begin by reading example A (numbers). Ask the subject to tell you one word that would name the three that you say. Use the carrier phrase *These are all* ______ to prompt the subject. If the subject responds correctly, read example B (money). If the subject responds with the wrong category word or names the numbers, state the target word and remind the subject of the nature of the task. Continue with the next example. Read example B (money) and say, *These are all* ______. If the subject responds correctly, read the starter items. If the subject does not name the target word, say *money* and continue with the starter items. Use the carrier phrase *These are all* ______ when reading the examples and starter items. Do not use the carrier phrase when reading the test items unless necessary to elicit a response.

Starter Items

Since the starter items are not test items, they are not included in the accuracy evaluation. As a result, they may be used if needed to teach the task to the subject. Beginning with starter item A, present the four starter items (birds, candy, days, and music). Use the carrier phrase *These are all* ______ with each starter item. Remind the subject: *Remember to give only one word in your answer.* Correct any errors made on the starter items. Following the starter items, continue with the test items. Use the carrier phrase *These are all* ______ when reading the examples and starter items. Do not use the carrier phrase when reading the test items unless necessary to elicit a response.

Test Items

Proceed with the test items. Read all the category items. Do not use the carrier phrase during testing unless a subject begins to repeat the three words given rather than the category word. If this occurs, remind the subject of the task, using the carrier phrase *These are all* ______. Item presentation should be fluent, and each reading should be made immediately following the subject's response. If a subject fails to respond in 15 seconds, move to the next item.

Marking Responses

Accuracy. With the response booklet open to Section 5, Category Naming, mark a "1" for all correct responses adjacent the test item. For all incorrect responses, record the subject's complete response in the space provided and record a "0" adjacent the test item in which there was an error.

Gestures. Gestures that indicate frustration with the naming task (snapping fingers, tapping, facial grimaces, etc.) or mime the target word (pointing to wrist for time or indicating eating for silverware, etc.) occurring while the subject attempts to find a target word, should be noted with one check (√) per test item in the *Gesture* column.

Extra Verbalizations. Any additional verbalizations ("um, oh, I forgot it," "I know it, but I can't think of it," etc.) made during the naming process should be noted with one check (√) for each item in the *Extra Verbal* column.

All other spaces and columns in the response booklet are to be completed after the test administration. In summary, during administration of Section 5, record responses in four of the columns on page 6 of the response booklet: *1 or 0, Subject's Response, Gesture,* and *Extra Verbal.*

SECTION 6, COMPREHENSION ASSESSMENT

The purpose of this section is to assess the subject's comprehension of those target words which he or she had difficulty naming on the five word-finding sections. By definition, subjects with word-finding problems have difficulty finding words in the presence of good comprehension of those target words. Therefore, because target-word comprehension must be present before a response error can be considered a word-finding error, target-word comprehension of all errors must be assessed. This assessment is performed after all five word-finding sections have been administered, particularly when the individual's accuracy score is low enough to indicate a possible word-finding deficit.

The vocabulary for the comprehension evaluation consists of all the target words on the TAWF. Each target word is presented with three decoys in a four-picture format. The comprehension tasks for a specific subject consist of pictures and sentences representing those target words on which the subject made errors. Note that any item in Section 1 that was accurately named within the 15-second interval is considered correct (regardless of whether it was named within the 4-second interval used to estimate item response time). The examiner should turn back in the response booklet to Section 1 and, noting the erred items, proceed in the test book to the pictures that correspond to the erred items and present the comprehension tasks (see Figure 2-8). This process is repeated for Sections 2 through 5. Remember, assessment of comprehension does not require naming, but uses a recognition response only.

Comprehension Assessment for Section 1, Picture Naming: Nouns

In this evaluation the focus is on assessing the subject's knowledge of the target words missed in the word-finding assessment in Section 1, Picture Naming: Nouns. Present the picture strips representing the items in Section 1 that are to be evaluated and state the phrase *Point to* ______ with the target word. The subject is to point to the appropriate picture in the strip of four pictures. Proceed in this manner until target-word comprehension of all errors in Section 1 is assessed.

Section 3
Description Naming

Starter Items

A. What is used for a bird's home, is made of small pieces of grass, and is found in a tree? (nest)

B. What do you find at the beach, is soft to walk on, and is used to build play castles? (sand)

C. What part of your face is used for eating, has teeth and a tongue, and is below your nose? (mouth)

D. What do you put on an envelope, is rectangular or square, and has glue on the back? (stamp)

Item	1 or 0		Subject's Response	Gesture (✓)	Extra Verbal (✓)	Sentence Comp[1]		Word Comp		Comp Summary		Response Code
	Brief Test	Complete Test				Yes (✓)	No	Yes (✓)	No	Yes (✓)	No	
1. What gives people a warning, is used on police cars and fire trucks, and makes a loud noise? (siren)		1										
2. What is a hat that is made of a hard material and is used to protect the head when playing football? (helmet)		1										
3. What is a permanent picture that is drawn on your skin by putting color in with a needle? (tattoo)		1										
4. What is a moving stairway that is found in a department store and that takes people up and down? (escalator)		1										
5. What is the name of a group of people chosen in court to hear evidence and give a verdict in a trial? (jury)		1										
6. What is a machine that may be shaped like a person and is programmed to do certain human jobs? (robot)		0	Um, I can't think			✓		✓		✓		
7. What do you plant in the ground that is small and hard and that grows into a flower or vegetable? (seed)		1										
8. What is the kind of clothing that is funny or strange and is worn on stage or for a special party? (costume)		0	tuxedo			✓		✓		✓		
9. What is the imaginary circle around the earth halfway between the North and South Poles? (equator)		1										
10. What is a large covered basket often found in your bedroom or bathroom in which you put dirty clothes? (hamper)		1										
11. What is the name of the hair that is cut short and brushed down over the forehead? (bangs)		1										
12. What is a long paddle made of wood that is used to move a boat through the water? (oar)		0	long flat thing			✓		✓		✓		

Brief Test Raw Score	RAW SCORE	Gesture Total	Extra Verbal Total	Comprehension Total
	9			0

(total unknown)

[1] Subject must receive a "Yes" for sentence *and* word comprehension to score "Yes" on summary. All other combinations receive a "No" on summary.

4

Figure 2-8. Recording responses for comprehension assessment of target words missed in Section 3.

Marking Responses

A subject's failure to identify the appropriate picture may be an indication of poor comprehension of that target word and should be checked "no," failure to comprehend the stimulus. The "no" score should be recorded across from the target word in the comprehension column on the response booklet. This check indicates that during the word-finding assessment, the subject may have made a naming error due to lack of knowledge rather than a word-finding problem. If the subject passed the item (a check in the "yes" column), target-word comprehension is judged adequate for a word-finding assessment and the error in the analysis is considered a word-finding error. Therefore, the item is checked "yes" across from the target word in the comprehension column in the response booklet.

Comprehension Assessment for Section 2, Sentence Completion Naming

For errors in Section 2, comprehension of both the sentence and the target word must be verified before a judgment of word-finding skills on a particular item can be made. Begin by turning to the picture strips of target words in Section 2. Comprehension of all sentence items missed should be assessed first (Phase 1), followed by an assessment of the subject's knowledge of the target words missed (Phase 2).

Comprehension Assessment of Sentence Items (Phase 1)

Read the following instructions to assess comprehension of the open-ended sentences:

I am going to read some sentences that will have the last word missing. Look at the pictures and point to the one that completes the sentence correctly.

Then read the open-ended sentence missed by the subject and instruct the subject to point to the picture of the word that best completes the sentence. Check the subject's comprehension of all sentence items missed.

Comprehension Assessment of Target Words (Phase 2)

After assessing comprehension of all sentence items on which there was a naming error, return to the first missed item in Section 2 and now check comprehension of the target words missed. Read to the subject:

This time I will tell you to point to a picture that I name. Look carefully at all the pictures and point to the correct picture.

Using the carrier phrase *Point to* ______ and the target word, ask the subject to identify the picture representing the given word. Check comprehension of all target words missed.

Marking Responses

In the comprehension evaluation, the examiner is interested in knowing if the subject understands both the sentence and the target word missed in the naming section. There are some individuals who may not understand the test sentence though they do know the target word. Discrepancies of this nature across several items should be noted, for they suggest that sentence comprehension difficulties underly the inability to name the target word rather than lack of knowledge of the target word itself. Therefore, a failure to identify the picture representing the sentence or the target word may be an indication of poor comprehension of the test item. Failure to comprehend the stimulus should be scored "no." Mark a check (√) in the "no" column for the word and for the sentence in the appropriate space adjacent the target word. However, if the subject passes the sentence and the target-word comprehension check, check "yes" in the appropriate comprehension column.

Comprehension Assessment for Section 3, Description Naming

For errors in Section 3 (like those in Section 2), comprehension of both the sentence and the target word must be verified before a judgment of word-finding skills on a particular item can be made. Begin by presenting the picture strips exhibiting pictures of target words in Section 3. Comprehension of all sentence items missed should be checked first (Phase 1), followed by an assessment of the subject's knowledge of the target words missed (Phase 2).

Comprehension Assessment of Description Items (Phase 1)

Read the following instructions to assess comprehension of the descriptions:

I am going to read a description of something to you. Look at the pictures and point to the picture that has been described.

Then read the description missed by the subject and instruct the subject to point to the picture of the word that best fits the description. Check comprehension of all sentence descriptions on which the subject erred.

Comprehension Assessment of Target Words (Phase 2)

After assessing comprehension of all sentence items on which there was a naming error, return to the first missed item in Section 3 and now check comprehension of the target words missed. Read to the subject:

This time I will tell you to point to a picture that I name. Look carefully at all the pictures and point to the correct picture.

Using the carrier phrase *Point to* ______ and the target word, ask the subject to identify the picture representing the given word. Check comprehension of all target words missed.

Marking Responses

In the comprehension evaluation, the examiner is interested in knowing if the subject understands both the sentence and the target words missed in the naming section. There are some individuals who may not understand the test sentence though they do know the target word. Discrepancies of this nature across several items should be noted, for they suggest that sentence comprehension difficulties underly the inability to name the target word rather than lack of knowledge of the target word itself. Therefore, a failure to identify the picture representing the sentence or the target word may be an indication of poor comprehension of the test item. Failure to comprehend the stimulus should be scored "no." Mark a check (√) in the "no" column for the word or for the sentence in the appropriate space adjacent the target word. However, if the subject passes the sentence and the target-word comprehension check, mark a check (√) in the "yes" column in the comprehension column for both the sentence and the target word.

Comprehension Assessment for Section 4, Picture Naming: Verbs

In this evaluation the focus is on assessing the subject's knowledge of the target words missed in the word-finding assessment in Section 4, Picture Naming: Verbs. Present the picture strips representing the items in Section 4 that are to be evaluated and state the phrase *Point to* ______ with the target word. The subject is to point to the appropriate picture in the strip of four pictures. Proceed in this manner until target-word comprehension of all errors in Section 4 is assessed.

Marking Responses

A failure to identify the appropriate pictures may be an indication of poor comprehension of a given target word and should be checked "no," failure to comprehend the stimulus. Check the "no" score across from the target word in the comprehension column in the response booklet. This score indicates that during the word-finding assessment the subject may have made a naming error due to lack of knowledge rather than a word-finding problem. If the subject passes the item, target-word comprehension is judged to be adequate for the word-finding assessment and the error in the analysis is considered a word-finding error. The item is checked "yes" across from the target word in the comprehension column in the response booklet.

Comprehension Assessment for Section 5, Category Naming

In this evaluation the focus is on assessing the subject's knowledge of the target words missed in the word-finding assessment in Section 5, Category Naming. Present the pictures representing the items in Section 5 that are to be checked and state the phrase *Point to* _____ with the target word. The subject is to point to the appropriate picture. Proceed in this manner until target-word comprehension of all errors in Section 5 is assessed.

Marking Responses

A subject's failure to identify the appropriate pictures may be an indication of poor comprehension of a target word and should be checked "no," failure to comprehend the stimulus. The "no" score should be recorded across from the target word in the comprehension column in the response booklet. This check indicates that during the word-finding assessment, the subject may have made a naming error due to lack of knowledge rather than a word-finding problem. If the subject passes the item, target-word comprehension is judged to be adequate for the word-finding assessment and the error in the analysis is considered a word-finding error. Therefore, the item is checked "yes" across from the target word in the comprehension column in the response booklet.

CHAPTER THREE

SCORING PROCEDURES

This chapter provides the examiner with the scoring procedures for the TAWF. It is designed to aid the examiner in completing the TAWF *Response Booklet.* Specific guidelines are presented for recording important identification information, completing formal and informal scoring procedures, and determining appropriate word-finding profiles for the subject under study.

IDENTIFICATION INFORMATION

The examiner should begin by verifying the identification information in the top portion of the first page of the TAWF response booklet for the person being evaluated. Enter a student's name, school, grade placement, teacher, and examiner. Also indicate the referral source and the student's parents' names, address, and phone number. For an adult under study, enter his or her name, address, phone number, name of spouse, referral source, and examiner's name. Calculate the chronological age by subtracting the individual's birthdate from the test date, in the spaces provided, according to these guidelines:

1. when the number of days in the chronological age is greater than 15, add one month to the age;
2. when the number of days in the chronological age is less than 15 days, disregard days;
3. when borrowing days, always borrow 30 days; and
4. when borrowing months, always borrow 12 months.

See Figure 3-1 for a sample of student identification information.

NATIONAL COLLEGE OF EDUCATION

RESPONSE BOOKLET

TEST OF ADOLESCENT/ADULT WORD FINDING

TAWF

Diane J. German, Ph.D.

Name Art Example

School Lincoln Senior High Grade 10

Examiner Judy Katz

Teacher Donna Lynn

Referred by Ethel Newman

Address 613 S. Michigan St.

Geoffry, IL Phone 123-4567

Parent/Guardian/Spouse/Caretaker Eva + Ben Example

	Year	Month	Day
Test Date	88 ~~89~~	12 ~~4~~ =16	10
(−) Birthdate	72	8	6
(=) Age	16	8	4 *

*If the number of days exceeds 15, add a month to the age.

☐ Brief Test

☒ Complete Test

If following up the Brief Test with the complete test, record the complete test results in a different color.

Figure 3-1. Sample of student identification information recorded on the TAWF *Response Booklet* (response booklet, page 1).

ACCURACY SCORE SUMMARY

This section guides the examiner in the scoring of the individual's accuracy in naming. Specific scoring procedures for each naming section are presented, and guidelines for completing the Accuracy Score Summary follow.

ACCURACY RAW SCORES FOR SECTION 1, PICTURE NAMING: NOUNS

After the TAWF has been administered, review the responses recorded in the response booklet. On the TAWF, all *test* items are scored. Do not score examples or starter items. Opposite the target word indicate with a "1" or "0" whether the subject passed or failed the test item. (See Appendix B for scoring guidelines.) Always score the individual's *first response.* Self-corrections of first responses are scored as incorrect.

Any substitution for the target word is counted as an error except for visual misperception errors or acceptable substitutions. An example of a visual misperception error is *black dot* for *dice.* Examples of acceptable substitutions include *mike* for *microphone, field glasses* for *binoculars,* and *aerial* for *antenna.* A complete list of errors and acceptable substitutions for Section 1 target words is presented in Appendix B.

After scoring the responses, tally the number of correct responses (1's) and enter this total accuracy score in the raw score box at the bottom of page 2 in the response booklet. (See Figure 3-2 for an example of how to calculate raw scores for a sample subject, Art.) Transfer the Section 1 accuracy raw score to the space provided on the cover of the response booklet.

ACCURACY RAW SCORES FOR SECTION 2, SENTENCE COMPLETION NAMING

After the TAWF has been administered, review the responses recorded for Section 2 in the response booklet. All *test* items in Section 2 are scored. Do not score examples or starter items. Opposite the target word indicate with a "1" or "0" whether the subject passed or failed the test item. (See Appendix B for scoring guidelines.) Always score the individual's *first response.* Self-corrections of first responses are scored as incorrect. Generally, a substitution for a target word is counted as an error except when indicated as an acceptable substitution. Errors and acceptable substitutions for target words are presented in Appendix B. Tally the number of correct responses (1's) and enter this accuracy raw score (total correct) in the raw score box at the bottom of page 3 in the response

Section 1
Picture Naming: Nouns

Starter Items

A. nose B. thumb C. kite D. whistle

Item	1 or 0: Brief Test	1 or 0: Complete Test	Subject's Response	Item Response Time: ☐ Estimated During Testing: Less Than 4 sec. (✓)	Item Response Time: ☐ Estimated During Testing: More Than 4 sec. (✓)	Item Response Time: ☐ Actual from Tape Recording (sec/hun) (after testing)	Ges. (✓)	Ex. Ver. (✓)	Comprehension Yes (✓)	Comprehension No	Response Code (after testing)
1. ruler		1				/					
2. mask		1				/					
3. antenna		1				/					
4. statue		0				/					
5. crutch		1				/					
6. suspenders		1				/					
7. calculator		0				/					
8. palm		1				/					
9. microphone		1				/					
10. dice		1				/					
11. chopsticks		1				/					
12. battery		0				/					
13. eyebrow		1				/					
14. binoculars		1				/					
15. dart		1				/					
16. magnet		1				/					
17. acorn		0				/					
18. igloo		1				/					
19. starfish		0				/					
20. film		0				/					
21. backpack		1				/					
22. unicorn		1				/					
23. harmonica		1				/					
24. wishbone		0				/					
25. propeller		1				/					
26. jack		0				/					
27. thimble		1				/					
28. compass		0				/					
29. funnel		0				/					
30. pliers		0				/					
31. dustpan		1				/					
32. hopscotch		1				/					
33. blimp		1				/					
34. thermos		0				/					
35. tambourine		0				/					
36. spatula		1				/					
37. seahorse		0				/					

Brief Test Raw Score	RAW SCORE	Total Delayed Items	Total Item Response Time	Ges. Total	Ex. Ver. Total	Comprehension Total
	23		/			(total unknown)

2

Figure 3-2. Calculating the accuracy raw score on Section 1 (response booklet, page 2).

booklet. Transfer the Section 2 accuracy raw score to the space provided on the cover of the response booklet.

ACCURACY RAW SCORES FOR SECTION 3, DESCRIPTION NAMING

After the TAWF has been administered, review the responses recorded for Section 3 in the response booklet. All *test* items in Section 3 are scored. Do not score examples or starter items. Opposite the target word indicate with a "1" or "0" whether the subject passed or failed the test item. (See Appendix B for scoring guidelines.) Always score the individual's *first response.* Self-corrections of first responses are scored as incorrect. Generally, a substitution for a target word is counted as an error except when indicated as an acceptable substitution. Errors and acceptable substitutions for target words are presented in Appendix B. Tally the number of correct responses (1's) and enter this accuracy raw score (total correct) in the raw score box at the bottom of page 4 in the response booklet. Transfer the Section 3 accuracy raw score to the space provided on the cover of the response booklet.

ACCURACY RAW SCORES FOR SECTION 4, PICTURE NAMING: VERBS

After the TAWF has been administered, review the responses recorded for Section 4 in the response booklet. All *test* items in Section 4 are scored. Do not score examples or starter items. Opposite the target word indicate with a "1" or "0" whether the subject passed or failed the test item. (See Appendix B for scoring guidelines.) Always score the individual's *first response.* Self-corrections of first responses are scored as incorrect.

Any substitution for the target word is counted as an error except for visual misperceptions, root-word verbs, and acceptable substitutions. Acceptable substitutions include *shredding* for *grating, unplugging* for *plugging,* and *plaiting* for *braiding.* A complete list of errors and acceptable substitutions for target words in Section 4 is presented in Appendix B.

Tally the number of correct responses (1's) and enter this accuracy raw score (total correct) in the raw score box at the bottom of page 5 in the response booklet. Transfer the Section 4 accuracy raw score to the space provided on the cover of the response booklet.

ACCURACY RAW SCORES FOR SECTION 5, CATEGORY NAMING

After the TAWF has been administered, review the responses recorded for Section 5 in the response booklet. All *test* items in Section 5 are scored. Do not score examples or starter items. Opposite the target word indicate with a "1" or

"0" whether the subject passed or failed the test item. (See Appendix B for scoring guidelines.) Always score the individual's *first response*. Self-corrections of first responses are scored as incorrect.

Any substitution for the target word is counted as an error except for acceptable substitutions. Examples of acceptable substitutions include *vehicles* for *transportation* and *utensils* for *silverware*. A complete list of errors and acceptable substitutions for target words in Section 5 is presented in Appendix B.

Tally the number of correct responses (1's) and enter this accuracy raw score (total correct) in the raw score box at the bottom of page 6 in the response booklet. Transfer the Section 5 accuracy raw score to the space provided on the cover of the response booklet.

DETERMINING THE TOTAL RAW SCORE

The examiner should record the accuracy raw scores for each section in the space designated in the Accuracy Score Summary on the cover of the response booklet. Mean raw scores and standard deviations for each naming section are presented in Appendix E by grade- and age-level groupings. However, individual accuracy scores from the five naming sections must be totaled to obtain the derived scores on the TAWF. The examiner should sum the five section accuracy raw scores and enter this sum in the response booklet in the space labeled *TOTAL RAW SCORE*. Figure 3-3 presents an example of how to determine the total raw score for the sample subject.

Accuracy Score Summary

Section	Raw Score: Brief Test	Raw Score: Complete Test
1. Picture Naming: Nouns		23
2. Sentence Completion Naming		12
3. Description Naming		9
4. Picture Naming: Verbs		13
5. Category Naming		17
TOTAL RAW SCORE		74

Figure 3-3. Determining the total raw score for accuracy (response booklet, page 1).

CONVERTING THE RAW SCORE TO DERIVED SCORES

The examiner should next convert the raw score to the derived scores. Two derived scores are used on the TAWF: standard scores and percentile ranks. Because the TAWF was standardized on both grade and age reference groups, standard scores and percentiles are presented as a function of grade level and chronological age. Use of grade norms allows the examiner to compare a student's test results to the TAWF scores of those in the same grade in the standardization sample. Age norms allow the examiner to compare an individual's TAWF scores with the results of adolescents and adults of the same chronological age in the standardization sample.

The TAWF *Technical Manual* presents detailed information about the research and procedures used to develop the TAWF norms. The adolescent normative data are presented in standard scores and percentile ranks by grade levels 7 through 12 and by age intervals from 12 years 0 months through 19 years 11 months. Adult normative data are also presented in standard scores and percentile ranks by age intervals 20 years 0 months to 39 years 11 months, 40 years 0 months to 59 years 11 months, and 60 years 0 months to 80 years 0 months. Standard errors of measurement for each TAWF standard score are also provided. Norm Tables 1 through 7 are located in this manual following References.

To determine standard scores, locate the age-level interval in Norm Table 1 or the grade level in Norm Table 2 appropriate for the individual under study. For an adult, locate the age-level interval in Norm Table 3 that includes the adult's age. Enter the table by locating the individual's total raw score in the left column. Reading across from the raw score, locate the corresponding standard score in the standard score column. This represents the individual's standard score for accuracy. Record this score in the appropriate space provided in the Accuracy Score Summary on the cover of the response booklet (see Figure 3-4). Note that if a subject receives a raw score lower than the lowest value given in the appropriate table, the standard score assigned is recorded as "less than" the lowest standard score shown.

STANDARD ERROR OF MEASUREMENT AND RANGE OF CONFIDENCE SCORES

The TAWF is designed to be used in making significant decisions about an individual's expressive language skills; therefore, interpretation of an obtained score should consider measurement error. Measurement error occurs because diagnostic instruments, although reliable, have some degree of error and an individual's test behavior varies from assessment to assessment. The statistic commonly used to account for measurement error is the Standard Error of

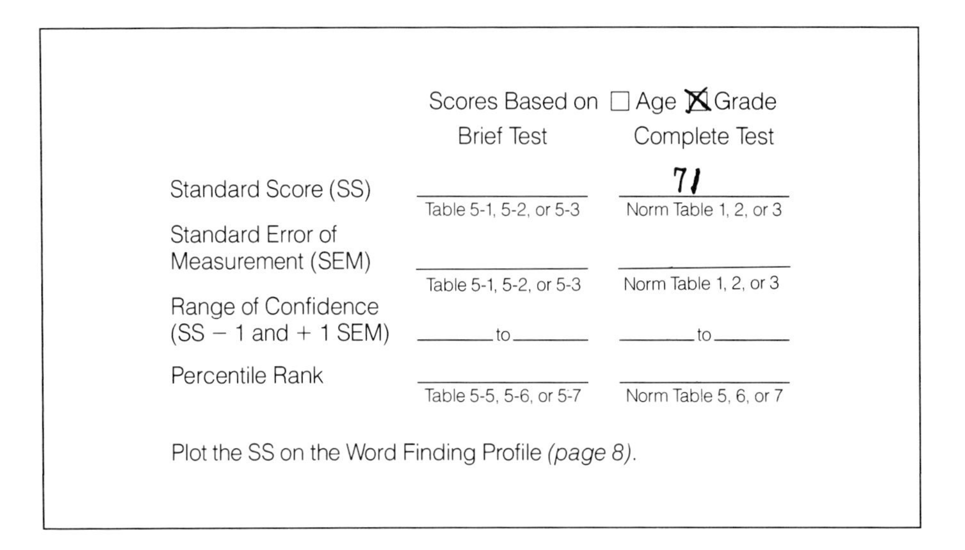
Scores Based on ☐ Age ☒ Grade

	Brief Test	Complete Test
Standard Score (SS)	______ Table 5-1, 5-2, or 5-3	71 Norm Table 1, 2, or 3
Standard Error of Measurement (SEM)	______ Table 5-1, 5-2, or 5-3	______ Norm Table 1, 2, or 3
Range of Confidence (SS − 1 and + 1 SEM)	____ to ____	____ to ____
Percentile Rank	______ Table 5-5, 5-6, or 5-7	______ Norm Table 5, 6, or 7

Plot the SS on the Word Finding Profile *(page 8)*.

Figure 3-4. Recording standard scores (response booklet, page 1).

Measurement (SEM), further discussed in the technical manual. It is recommended that the examiner use the SEM for an individual's obtained score as a basis for establishing a range of confidence within which the individual's true score can be expected to be found. The examiner needs to identify the SEM for the particular standard score obtained by the individual under study before this range of confidence can be established. Standard errors of measurement for each possible standard score on the TAWF are presented in Norm Table 4. Enter the appropriate table at the individual's standard score and locate the SEM reported for that score. Then record the SEM in the appropriate space in the Accuracy Score Summary.

Next, the examiner should determine the range of confidence for the obtained standard score. To calculate the upper and lower limits of the range of confidence, subtract the recorded SEM from the standard score and enter this lower limit in the appropriate space in the Accuracy Score Summary; then add the SEM to the standard score and record this upper limit in the response booklet (see Figure 3-5). This range of confidence is the individual's standard score range.

PERCENTILE RANK

To determine an adolescent's percentile ranks, locate the age-level interval in Norm Table 5 or the grade level in Norm Table 6 appropriate for the individual under study. For an adult, locate the age-level interval in Norm Table 7 that contains the subject's age. Enter the table by locating the individual's total raw score in the left column. Reading across from the raw score, locate the

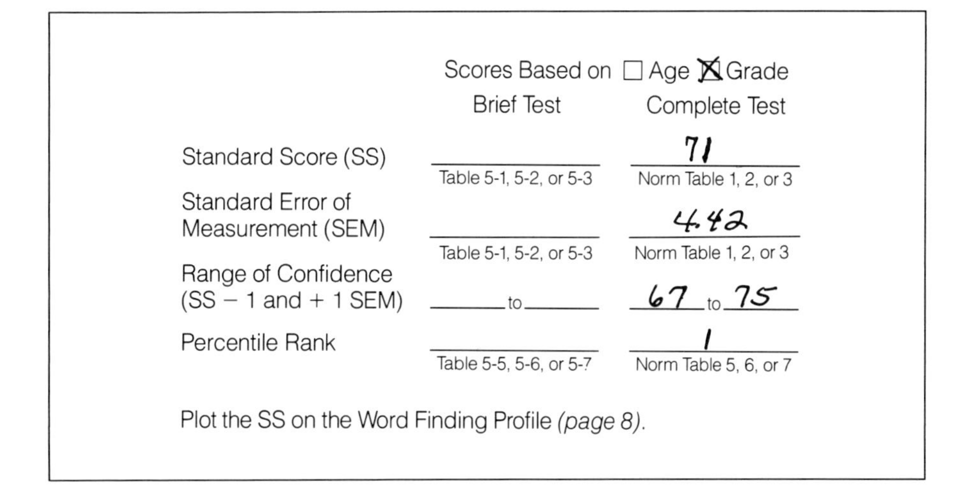

Scores Based on ☐ Age ☒ Grade

	Brief Test	Complete Test
Standard Score (SS)	______ (Table 5-1, 5-2, or 5-3)	71 (Norm Table 1, 2, or 3)
Standard Error of Measurement (SEM)	______ (Table 5-1, 5-2, or 5-3)	4.42 (Norm Table 1, 2, or 3)
Range of Confidence (SS − 1 and + 1 SEM)	____ to ____	67 to 75
Percentile Rank	______ (Table 5-5, 5-6, or 5-7)	1 (Norm Table 5, 6, or 7)

Plot the SS on the Word Finding Profile *(page 8)*.

Figure 3-5. Recording standard errors of measurement, ranges of confidence, and percentile ranks (response booklet, page 1).

corresponding percentile rank in the percentile rank column. This represents the individual's percentile rank for accuracy. The examiner should record the percentile score in the appropriate space provided in the Accuracy Score Summary on the cover of the response booklet (see Figure 3-5). After completing the Accuracy Score Summary, complete the interpretation section on page 8 to identify the appropriate Word Finding Profile.

COMPLETING RESPONSE-TIME EVALUATION

The purpose of the response-time evaluation is to measure a subject's speed in naming. There are two procedures that can be used individually or together to determine speed of naming on the TAWF: (1) the Estimated Item Response Time procedure and (2) the Actual Item Response Time measurement. **The examiner need use only one of these response-time evaluations.** Both utilize normative data from the standardization sample.

ESTIMATED ITEM RESPONSE TIME PROCEDURE

The Estimated Item Response Time procedure is used to judge the amount of time it takes a subject to name a target word in Section 1, Picture Naming: Nouns. It is determined by judging whether the period between the presentation of each stimulus picture and the individual's first effort to name the target word is greater than or less than 4 seconds. The Estimated Item Response Time procedure is completed during the TAWF administration of Section 1. For each item, the examiner judges whether the time between the verbalization of the word NOW and the subject's response is greater than or less than 4 seconds. The examiner simply checks the column adjacent the target item that represents whether the period was greater than or less than the 4-second cutoff. For those items to which the subject did not respond within the 15-second time limit, the examiner would indicate that the estimated item response time was greater than the 4-second criterion. See Appendix F for the grade- and age-level standards for the number of response delays (4 seconds or longer) representing the slowest 20% of each group in the standardization sample. (See Tables 3-13 through 3-16 in the TAWF *Technical Manual* for means and standard deviations for the item response times for each item in Section 1 by grade and age groupings.)

After administering all of the items in Section 1, complete the Estimated Item Response Time procedure by tallying the number of delayed responses (those whose item response time was estimated to be 4 seconds or more); that is, tally the number of checks in the "more than" column. Enter this number in the appropriate space at the bottom of page 2 in the response booklet. (See Figure 3-6 for an example of how to tally Estimated Item Response Time judgments.) Transfer this number to the space provided on the cover of the response booklet.

ACTUAL ITEM RESPONSE TIME MEASUREMENT (Optional)

The optional Actual Item Response Time measurement is an actual measurement of the time it takes the subject to name each picture in Section 1. It is determined by measuring to a hundredth of a second the time between the presentation of each picture stimulus and the individual's first effort to name each target word. The Average Item Response Time (ART) measurement is the sum of these item response times divided by the number of items administered (37 items). **Measurement of an individual's Actual Item Response Time is completed after the TAWF has been administered. Do not measure a subject's Actual Item Response Time while administering the TAWF.** Because the Actual Item Response Time measurement is made from an audio tape recording of Section 1, the examiner will need both the tape recording of the individual's responses in Section 1 and a stopwatch. The presentation of the picture can be identified on the audio tape by the examiner's verbalization of the word NOW as the picture was presented. The response-time measurement is the time, measured to the nearest hundredth of a second, between the word NOW and the individual's response. Response time should be recorded in the space provided for each item in Section 1 (page 2 of the response booklet). **For those items to which the individual did not respond within the 15-second time limit, the examiner assigns 15 seconds as the Actual Item Response Time.** During administration, the

Section 1
Picture Naming: Nouns

Starter Items A. nose B. thumb C. kite D. whistle

Item	1 or 0		Subject's Response	Item Response Time			Ges. (✓)	Ex. Ver. (✓)	Comprehension Yes (✓) No		Response Code (after testing)
				☒ Estimated During Testing		☐ Actual from Tape Recording (sec/hun) (after testing)					
	Brief Test	Complete Test		Less Than 4 sec. (✓)	More Than 4 sec. (✓)				Yes	No	
1. ruler		1		✓		/					
2. mask		1			✓	/					
3. antenna		1		✓		/					
4. statue		0	man on a horse		✓	/					
5. crutch		1		✓		/					
6. suspenders		1		✓		/					
7. calculator		0	computer	✓		/					
8. palm		1		✓		/					
9. microphone		1		✓		/					
10. dice		1		✓		/					
11. chopsticks		1		✓		/					
12. battery		0	box		✓	/					
13. eyebrow		1		✓		/					
14. binoculars		1			✓	/					
15. dart		1		✓		/					
16. magnet		1		✓		/					
17. acorn		0	fruit		✓	/					
18. igloo		1		✓		/					
19. starfish		0	shellfish	✓		/					
20. film		0	tape	✓		/					
21. backpack		1		✓		/					
22. unicorn		1		✓		/					
23. harmonica		1		✓		/					
24. wishbone		0	I don't know		✓	/					
25. propeller		1		✓		/					
26. jack		0	lifter		✓	/					
27. thimble		1		✓		/					
28. compass		0	directions	✓		/					
29. funnel		0	siphon		✓	/					
30. pliers		0	wrench	✓		/					
31. dustpan		1		✓		/					
32. hopscotch		1		✓		/					
33. blimp		1			✓	/					
34. thermos		0	coffee cup	✓		/					
35. tambourine		0	drum	✓		/					
36. spatula		1		✓		/					
37. seahorse		0	dragon fish		✓	/					

Brief Test Raw Score	RAW SCORE	Total Delayed Items	Total Item Response Time	Ges. Total	Ex. Ver. Total	Comprehension Total
	23	10	/			(total unknown)

2

Figure 3-6. Completing the Estimated Item Response Time tally (response booklet, page 2).

examiner should be careful not to extend the response time allowed beyond the 15-second interval.

To facilitate the Actual Item Response Time measurement, an audio tape recorder with a pause button should be used. A pause button allows the examiner to start and stop the tape recorder easily. The following procedure is suggested. With one hand controlling the stopwatch and the other hand controlling the pause button, release the pause button and listen for the word NOW. Upon hearing NOW, start the watch and measure the time between the word NOW and the individual's first response for a given item (correct or incorrect). Stop the watch and push the pause button as soon as you hear the first response to the item. Record the time indicated on the stopwatch as the Actual Item Response Time measurement for the given target word. To continue, release the pause button again to hear the next NOW and measure the item response time for the next item, following the same procedures. With practice, these procedures become manageable. If an examiner intends to use the Actual Item Response Time procedure, it is recommended that he or she complete five practice trials to gain facility with these procedures. These five practice trials can be completed on the same audio tape.

The Total Item Response Time is the sum of the individual actual item response times for the items in Section 1 (37 items). The Total Item Response Time is calculated by adding these individual times.

The Average Item Response Time (ART) refers to an individual's average response time for all Section 1 items. The ART is calculated by dividing the Total Item Response Time by the number of items administered in Section 1 (37). The ART is calculated and recorded in the space provided in the Item Response Time Summary on page 1 of the response booklet. (See Figure 3-7 for an example of how to complete the Item Response Time Summary.)

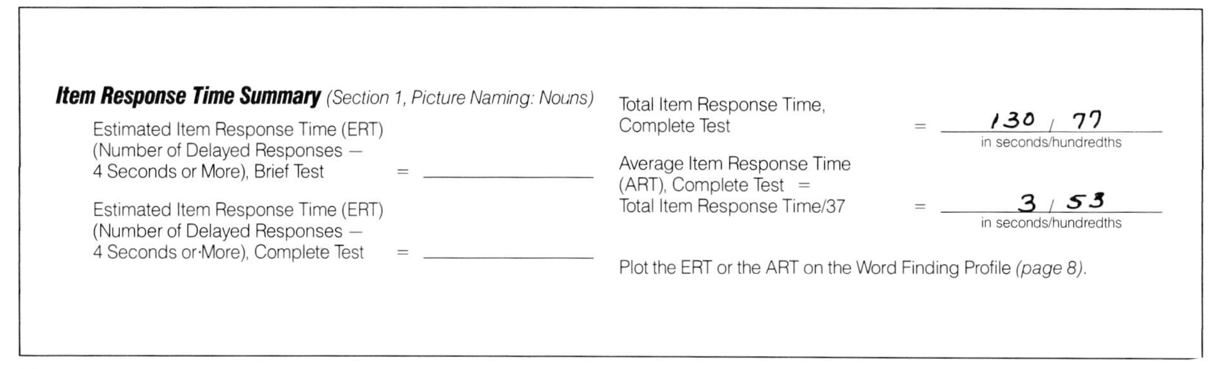
Item Response Time Summary *(Section 1, Picture Naming: Nouns)*

Estimated Item Response Time (ERT) (Number of Delayed Responses — 4 Seconds or More), Brief Test = ______

Estimated Item Response Time (ERT) (Number of Delayed Responses — 4 Seconds or More), Complete Test = ______

Total Item Response Time, Complete Test = 130 / 77 (in seconds/hundredths)

Average Item Response Time (ART), Complete Test = Total Item Response Time/37 = 3 / 53 (in seconds/hundredths)

Plot the ERT or the ART on the Word Finding Profile *(page 8)*.

Figure 3-7. Completing the Item Response Time Summary (response booklet, page 1).

COMPLETING THE WORD FINDING PROFILE

The last page of the response booklet (page 8) contains the accuracy and time chart for completing the TAWF Word Finding Profile. This chart allows the examiner to plot a subject's accuracy standard score with either the subject's Estimated Item Response Time index (ERT) or the Average Item Response Time (ART) to establish his or her Word Finding Profile. (The examiner need complete only one of these response-time measurements.) These profiles, discussed further in Chapter 4, include *Profile A, Fast and Inaccurate Namer; Profile B, Slow and Inaccurate Namer; Profile C, Fast and Accurate Namer* (no word-finding problems on the TAWF); and *Profile D, Slow and Accurate Namer.*

To complete the Word Finding Profile, follow these guidelines:

1. Transfer the subject's standard score from the Accuracy Score Summary on the front page of the response booklet to the appropriate space next to the Word Finding Profile on page 8. The examiner may choose the standard score based on grade or age norms, checking the appropriate box for age or grade on page 8.
2. If using the Estimated Item Response Time (ERT) procedure, transfer the ERT from page 1 to the space provided on page 8. Then circle the ERT, whether for the complete TAWF or for the TAWF Brief Test, in the appropriate grade- or age-level row in the grid near the top of the page.
3. If using the Actual Item Response Time measurement, transfer the Average Item Response Time (ART) from page 1 to the space provided on page 8. Then circle the ART in the appropriate grade- or age-level row in the grid near the bottom of the page. Note that the ART can be used only with the complete TAWF.
4. Identify the subject's accuracy standard score in the column to the left of the profile and circle it or the nearest approximation.
5. Find the intersection of the subject's accuracy standard score and his or her ERT or ART and shade in the intersection. Note the quadrant (A, B, C, or D) in which the subject's indices fall. The label of this quadrant represents the subject's word-finding profile. Note that borderline ranges (light shading) are indicated on the profile chart for those examiners who wish to apply a more liberal interpretation to their subject's accuracy or time scores due to unique qualities of a particular individual. For ERT scores, these borderline ranges represent a larger or smaller percentage of the standardization sample classified as "slow." That is, the ERT value at the lower boundary of the borderline range represents the ERT obtained by the slowest 30% of the sample; the ERT value at the upper boundary of the borderline range represents the ERT obtained by the slowest 10% of the sample. For ART scores, these borderline ranges represent scores that fall in the range of confidence for the cutoff score (which is one standard deviation above the mean). For accuracy scores, these borderline ranges represent those scores

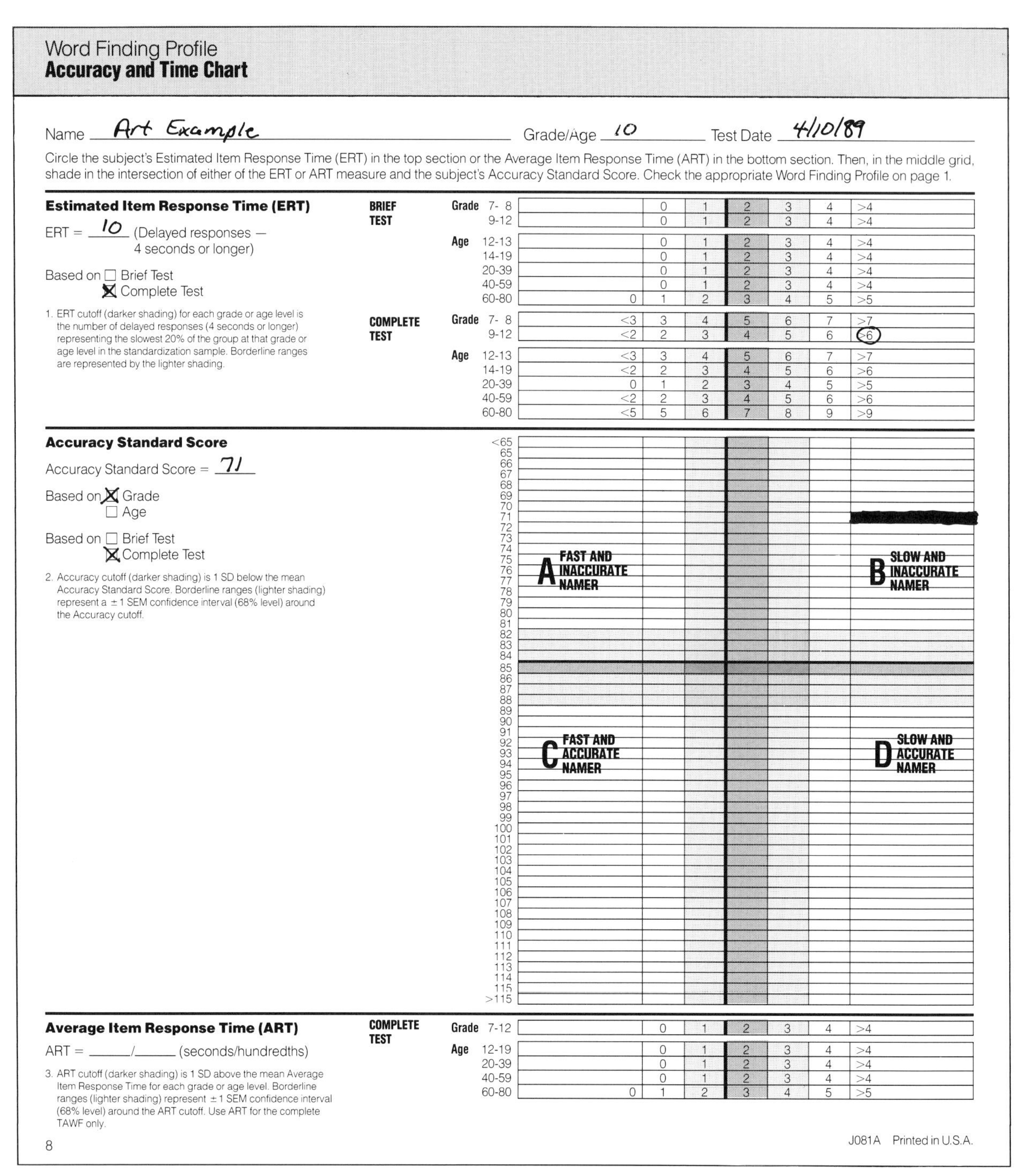

Word Finding Profile
Accuracy and Time Chart

Name Art Example Grade/Age 10 Test Date 4/10/89

Circle the subject's Estimated Item Response Time (ERT) in the top section or the Average Item Response Time (ART) in the bottom section. Then, in the middle grid, shade in the intersection of either of the ERT or ART measure and the subject's Accuracy Standard Score. Check the appropriate Word Finding Profile on page 1.

Estimated Item Response Time (ERT)

ERT = 10 (Delayed responses — 4 seconds or longer)

Based on ☐ Brief Test
☒ Complete Test

1. ERT cutoff (darker shading) for each grade or age level is the number of delayed responses (4 seconds or longer) representing the slowest 20% of the group at that grade or age level in the standardization sample. Borderline ranges are represented by the lighter shading.

Test	Level							
BRIEF TEST	Grade 7- 8		0	1	2	3	4	>4
	9-12		0	1	2	3	4	>4
	Age 12-13		0	1	2	3	4	>4
	14-19		0	1	2	3	4	>4
	20-39		0	1	2	3	4	>4
	40-59		0	1	2	3	4	>4
	60-80	0	1	2	3	4	5	>5
COMPLETE TEST	Grade 7- 8	<3	3	4	5	6	7	>7
	9-12	<2	2	3	4	5	6	>6
	Age 12-13	<3	3	4	5	6	7	>7
	14-19	<2	2	3	4	5	6	>6
	20-39	0	1	2	3	4	5	>5
	40-59	<2	2	3	4	5	6	>6
	60-80	<5	5	6	7	8	9	>9

Accuracy Standard Score

Accuracy Standard Score = 71

Based on ☒ Grade
☐ Age

Based on ☐ Brief Test
☒ Complete Test

2. Accuracy cutoff (darker shading) is 1 SD below the mean Accuracy Standard Score. Borderline ranges (lighter shading) represent a ± 1 SEM confidence interval (68% level) around the Accuracy cutoff.

<65 65 66 67 68 69 70 71 72 73 74 75 76 77 78 79 80 81 82 83 84 85 86 87 88 89 90 91 92 93 94 95 96 97 98 99 100 101 102 103 104 105 106 107 108 109 110 111 112 113 114 115 >115

A FAST AND INACCURATE NAMER

B SLOW AND INACCURATE NAMER

C FAST AND ACCURATE NAMER

D SLOW AND ACCURATE NAMER

Average Item Response Time (ART)

ART = ____/____ (seconds/hundredths)

3. ART cutoff (darker shading) is 1 SD above the mean Average Item Response Time for each grade or age level. Borderline ranges (lighter shading) represent ± 1 SEM confidence interval (68% level) around the ART cutoff. Use ART for the complete TAWF only.

Test	Level							
COMPLETE TEST	Grade 7-12		0	1	2	3	4	>4
	Age 12-19		0	1	2	3	4	>4
	20-39		0	1	2	3	4	>4
	40-59		0	1	2	3	4	>4
	60-80	0	1	2	3	4	5	>5

8

J081A Printed in U.S.A.

Figure 3-8. Completed Word Finding Profile (response booklet, page 8).

that fall in the range of confidence for the cutoff score of 85 (one standard deviation below the mean). The accuracy and ART confidence ranges are equivalent to 1 SEM, thus providing a 68% level of confidence. Subjects whose scores fall in these ranges may be interpreted as borderline slow or borderline inaccurate in naming, but should also be observed in other expressive language situations to clarify their word-finding skills in constrained naming.

6. Check the box at the bottom of the front page of the response booklet that corresponds to the subject's word-finding profile.

Figure 3-8 shows the completed Word Finding Profile for Art. Note that he received a standard score of 71 and an ERT score of 10. When plotted, these scores intersect in the quadrant labeled *Slow and Inaccurate Namer.* Thus, Art's word-finding skills are classified as typical of Profile B, Slow and Inaccurate. Appendix A contains Art's completed response booklet, including the front page.

INFORMAL ASSESSMENT OF WORD FINDING

COMPLETING THE COMPREHENSION SUMMARY

After completing the Accuracy Score Summary and the Item Response Time Summary, the examiner should complete the Comprehension Summary. If an individual under study reveals a TAWF profile suggestive of word-finding problems, the percentage of target-word comprehension should be calculated in order to determine if the individual knows the target words he or she was unable to name in the word-finding sections. (See Chapters 1 and 2 for discussions of comprehension assessment.)

To complete the comprehension assessment, the examiner must determine the number of target words the individual under study did not know. Begin by tallying all comprehension items checked "no" (for fail) in each of the five naming sections. For Sections 1, 4, and 5, this consists of adding the number of checks in the "no" column under comprehension. Enter the total (number of unknown words) in the space provided for the comprehension total at the bottom of the comprehension column for each of these sections. For Sections 2 and 3, a failure to comprehend both the sentence and the word results in a "no" score for an item. To tally these sections, add the number of "no" checks for items on which the individual did not receive a "yes" for *both* sentence and word comprehension. Enter this total (number of unknown items) in the space provided for the comprehension total at the bottom of the comprehension column for these sections. Figure 3-9 illustrates the comprehension tally procedure for Section 3.

The examiner should next sum the comprehension totals (number unknown) in each section and enter this sum in the Comprehension Summary section on page 7 of the response booklet. This constitutes the number of unknown words or items in the comprehension assessment. Subtract this number of unknown

Section 3
Description Naming

Starter Items

A. What is used for a bird's home, is made of small pieces of grass, and is found in a tree? (nest)

B. What do you find at the beach, is soft to walk on, and is used to build play castles? (sand)

C. What part of your face is used for eating, has teeth and a tongue, and is below your nose? (mouth)

D. What do you put on an envelope, is rectangular or square, and has glue on the back? (stamp)

Item	1 or 0 Brief Test	1 or 0 Complete Test	Subject's Response	Gesture (✓)	Extra Verbal (✓)	Sentence Comp[1] Yes (✓)	Sentence Comp[1] No	Word Comp Yes (✓)	Word Comp No	Comp Summary Yes (✓)	Comp Summary No	Response Code
1. What gives people a warning, is used on police cars and fire trucks, and makes a loud noise? (siren)		1										
2. What is a hat that is made of a hard material and is used to protect the head when playing football? (helmet)		1										
3. What is a permanent picture that is drawn on your skin by putting color in with a needle? (tattoo)		1										
4. What is a moving stairway that is found in a department store and that takes people up and down? (escalator)		1										
5. What is the name of a group of people chosen in court to hear evidence and give a verdict in a trial? (jury)		1										
6. What is a machine that may be shaped like a person and is programmed to do certain human jobs? (robot)		0	Um, I can't think		✓	✓		✓		✓		NR
7. What do you plant in the ground that is small and hard and that grows into a flower or vegetable? (seed)		1										
8. What is the kind of clothing that is funny or strange and is worn on stage or for a special party? (costume)		0	tuxedo	✓		✓		✓		✓		PW
9. What is the imaginary circle around the earth halfway between the North and South Poles? (equator)		1										
10. What is a large covered basket often found in your bedroom or bathroom in which you put dirty clothes? (hamper)		1										
11. What is the name of the hair that is cut short and brushed down over the forehead? (bangs)		1										
12. What is a long paddle made of wood that is used to move a boat through the water? (oar)		0	long flat thing	✓		✓		✓		✓		C (VS)

Brief Test Raw Score	RAW SCORE	Gesture Total	Extra Verbal Total	Comprehension Total (total unknown)
	9	2	1	0

[1]Subject must receive a "Yes" for sentence *and* word comprehension to score "Yes" on summary. All other combinations receive a "No" on summary.

4

Figure 3-9. Tallying comprehension scores on Section 3 (response booklet, page 4).

items from the number of total test items to obtain the number of known items on the TAWF. To calculate the Percent of Comprehension, divide the number of known items by 107, the total number of TAWF test items (see Figure 3-10). (If using the Brief Test, subtract the number of unknown items from 40, the total number of Brief Test items, to obtain the number of items known on the Brief Test. Then divide the number of known items by 40.)

This comprehension percentage score is used to determine if the individual's percentage of comprehension is as high as his or her grade- or age-level counterparts in the standardization sample. For example, if an individual's percentage of comprehension is 90% or above, the individual demonstrated high comprehension on the TAWF items. For high comprehension, check "high" on page 1 of the response booklet. Results of 89% and below indicate a low comprehension score on the TAWF. For low comprehension, check "low" on page 1 of the response booklet. A check in the "high" box indicates that the individual's percentage of comprehension is as high as that of his or her grade- or age-level counterparts in the standardization sample. For this individual, the profile results on the TAWF may be considered a valid reflection of word-finding skills. However, if the "low" box is checked, the individual's percentage of comprehension on the TAWF is low; the naming errors may be due to lack of knowledge of the target words rather than a deficit in word finding. To help clarify the word-finding skills of an individual with a low comprehension score on the TAWF, the examiner should apply the Prorated Accuracy Rescoring procedure for low comprehension (presented below). See Figure 3-11 for an example of how to complete the Prorated Accuracy Rescoring procedure for an individual who has a low comprehension score on the TAWF.

The comprehension assessment will help professionals to differentiate between the three types of individuals who could manifest problems in finding words. The first is those who have word-finding difficulties in the presence of good understanding of language (this is the classical definition of word-finding disorders in children and adults). They thus have difficulty retrieving words that

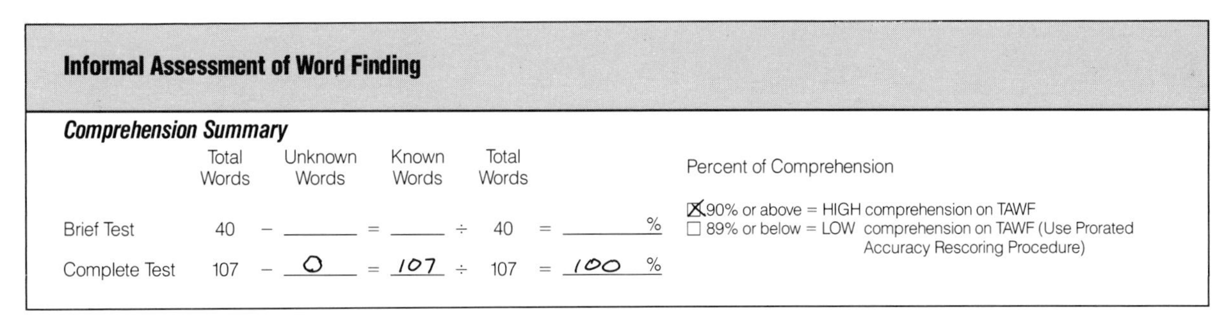

Informal Assessment of Word Finding

Comprehension Summary

	Total Words		Unknown Words		Known Words		Total Words		Percent of Comprehension
Brief Test	40	–	______	=	______	÷	40	=	______ %
Complete Test	107	–	0	=	107	÷	107	=	100 %

☒ 90% or above = HIGH comprehension on TAWF
☐ 89% or below = LOW comprehension on TAWF (Use Prorated Accuracy Rescoring Procedure)

Figure 3-10. Calculating percent of comprehension on the TAWF (response booklet, page 7).

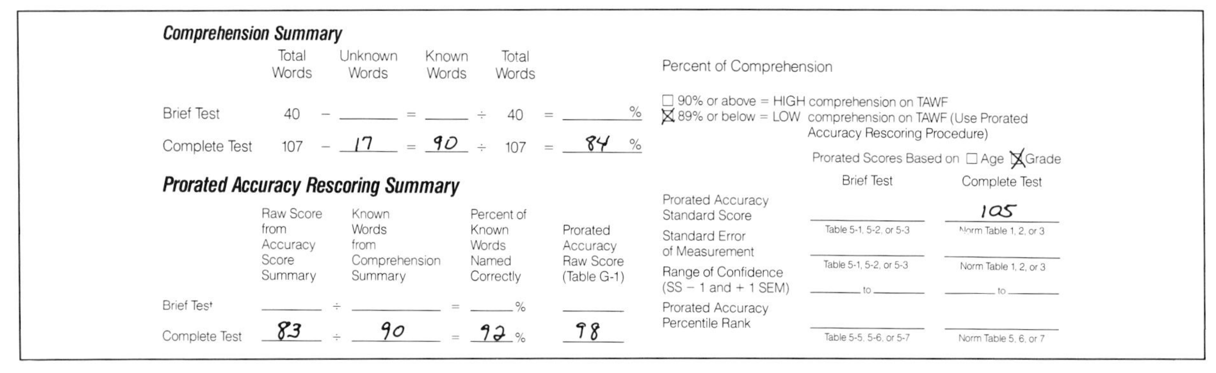

Comprehension Summary

	Total Words		Unknown Words		Known Words		Total Words		
Brief Test	40	−	____	=	____	÷	40	=	____ %
Complete Test	107	−	17	=	90	÷	107	=	84 %

Percent of Comprehension

☐ 90% or above = HIGH comprehension on TAWF
☒ 89% or below = LOW comprehension on TAWF (Use Prorated Accuracy Rescoring Procedure)

Prorated Accuracy Rescoring Summary

	Raw Score from Accuracy Score Summary		Known Words from Comprehension Summary		Percent of Known Words Named Correctly	Prorated Accuracy Raw Score (Table G-1)
Brief Test†	____	÷	____	=	____ %	____
Complete Test	83	÷	90	=	92 %	98

Prorated Scores Based on ☐ Age ☒ Grade

	Brief Test	Complete Test
Prorated Accuracy Standard Score	____ (Table 5-1, 5-2, or 5-3)	105 (Norm Table 1, 2, or 3)
Standard Error of Measurement	____ (Table 5-1, 5-2, or 5-3)	____ (Norm Table 1, 2, or 3)
Range of Confidence (SS − 1 and + 1 SEM)	____ to ____	____ to ____
Prorated Accuracy Percentile Rank	____ (Table 5-5, 5-6, or 5-7)	____ (Norm Table 5, 6, or 7)

Figure 3-11. Completing the Prorated Accuracy Rescoring procedure (response booklet, page 7).

they know. Identification of these individuals is straightforward as they will receive comprehension scores of 90 to 100% on the TAWF comprehension assessment and accuracy standard scores below 85 or in the borderline range of 80 to 90. Their comprehension scores on the TAWF are appropriate and one would not suspect underlying problems in understanding language. The individuals' accuracy scores reflect their expressive word-finding skills. If an individual's accuracy standard score is below 85 or within or below the borderline range of 80 to 90, one would identify him or her as an inaccurate namer.

There are also two other types of individuals who may earn low comprehension scores on the TAWF. Type 2 consists of those individuals who have problems understanding language and who manifest word-finding difficulties on words that they do not know or that are not stable in their receptive language. They do not manifest word-finding difficulties on words they know; these individuals have underlying problems in understanding language. Type 3 consists of those individuals who are "dually handicapped"; they have problems in understanding language and expressive word-finding problems. These individuals have difficulty finding words they don't know as well as manifest word-finding problems on words they do know (they have underlying problems in language comprehension and expressive language word-finding problems).

Differentiating these three types of problems is challenging. One of the major challenges in working with these problems is deciding whether an individual (a) has naming difficulties due to expressive language word-finding problems occurring in the presence of good understanding of language (Type 1), (b) has naming difficulties due to underlying language comprehension deficits (Type 2), or (c) has naming difficulties due to both underlying comprehension problems and expressive language deficits (Type 3). The Prorated Accuracy Rescoring procedure described below is used to help differentiate these three types of problems.

PRORATED ACCURACY RESCORING PROCEDURE FOR LOW COMPREHENSION

The Prorated Accuracy Rescoring procedure is recommended for an individual who does not meet the comprehension criterion recommended on the TAWF (comprehension scores below 90%). This informal procedure allows the examiner to rescore the response booklet to generate a prorated accuracy score. This new score simply represents the individual's naming accuracy on words he or she knew. The Prorated Accuracy Rescoring Summary is found on page 7 of the response booklet. It involves the following steps:

1. Compute the percentage of words known (comprehension score of yes) and named accurately (accuracy raw score of 1) by dividing the total Raw Score by the number of known words in the comprehension section. Record the percentage of known words named accurately in the space provided on page 7 of the response booklet.
2. Look up the Prorated Accuracy Raw Score in Table G-1. Locate the subject's Percentage of Known Words Named Accurately in the left-hand column, and read the Prorated Accuracy Raw Score from the middle column (complete test) or the right-hand column (Brief Test).
3. Look up the Prorated Accuracy Raw Score in the norms table for the subject's age or grade to find the subject's Prorated Accuracy Standard Score. This score represents naming accuracy on only those words the subject knew (as indicated in the comprehension section).
4. Enter the Prorated Accuracy Standard Score in the appropriate space on page 7 of the response booklet.
5. Compute the range of confidence and find the prorated Percentile Rank as you did for the initial standard scores for accuracy.

If, after rescoring an individual's response booklet, you find that the Prorated Accuracy Standard Score is above the Accurate/Inaccurate cutoff score of 85 or, if you are using borderline ranges, above the 80 to 90 borderline range around the cutoff, you could conclude that the individual made naming errors only on words that he or she does not know. This finding would be typical of subject Type 2 above, suggesting a potential problem in understanding language that is causing difficulty in finding words. This would not be a true expressive language word-finding deficit, because on words the individual knows, he or she does not have a word-finding deficit. Further assessment of language comprehension would be needed to clarify this person's language difficulties.

However, if after rescoring an individual's response booklet, you find that the Prorated Standard Score is still below 85, or within or below the 80 to 90 borderline range, you might suspect that this individual is Type 3, that is, dually handicapped with both problems in understanding language and an expressive word-finding disorder. You could conclude that this subject has word-finding problems on words that he or she knows and may also have comprehension problems, as suggested by the low scores in the comprehension assessment.

Further assessment of language comprehension would be needed to clarify this individual's comprehension skills.

Again, this Prorated Accuracy Rescoring procedure is appropriate for individuals who do not meet the comprehension criterion for the TAWF. It would be appropriate for subjects you suspect may have problems in understanding language, but whose expressive language word-finding skills are unclear. It would also be appropriate for bilingual students whom you know have low receptive vocabulary skills in standard English, but whose expressive language word-finding skills on known vocabulary are unclear.

GESTURES AND EXTRA VERBALIZATIONS SUMMARY

Gestures and extra verbalizations expressed by the individual when encountering naming difficulty are noted by the examiner on the response booklet during administration of the TAWF. These secondary characteristics are indicated by a check (√) in the appropriate column across from test items. It is not necessary to record the extra verbalizations verbatim or write the word *gestures*. After administering the test and analyzing formal test results, proceed to tally the number of gestures and extra verbalizations checked in each section. Record these totals in the spaces provided at the bottom of each section in the response booklet. Transfer the total number of gestures and extra verbalizations to the summary in the informal assessment section on page 7. Add the five section totals and enter the sum in the space provided. Determine the percentage of items during which the individual demonstrated gestures and extra verbalizations by dividing the sums by the number of TAWF test items (107) and record the percentage in the designated box. See Chapter 4 and Appendix A for an interpretation and examples of these findings.

SUBSTITUTION TYPE SUMMARY

An informal evaluation that is useful in the identification of individuals with word-finding problems is the analysis of the types of substitutions they manifest when they are having difficulty naming target words. This analysis complements the accuracy assessment and should be completed on those subjects whose standard scores are below 85 or are in the 80 to 90 borderline range in the presence of a comprehension score that is 90% or above. For those individuals whose comprehension score is low, analyze the response substitutions of those target words that were misnamed during the test but known during the TAWF comprehension assessment. In this evaluation the examiner looks for naming patterns that may be unique to the person under study. During administration of the TAWF, the examiner should record the individual's actual responses in the response booklet when the individual makes a naming error. After administering the

TAWF, categorize each response in Sections 1, 2, 3, and 5 according to the categories listed below. Using the code for each response category, enter the response code in the far-right column in each section of the response booklet. (Further explanation and examples of the substitution response categories can be found in Chapter 4, with descriptions and examples also presented in Appendices B and C.)

Substitution Response Categories for Sections 1, 2, 3, and 5:

SUP = Superordinate
CO = Coordinate
SUB = Subordinate
FA = Functional Attribute
LA = Locative Attribute
COM = Compositional Attribute
A = Association
CH = Chained
PA = Phonemic Attribute
IS = Initial Sound
VS = Visual Substitution
VP = Visual Misperception
PW = Part/Whole
R = Repetition
AA = Acoustic Attribute
IN = Indefinite Noun
GN = General Noun
UN = Unspecified Noun
C = Circumlocution
SC = Substitution plus Self-Correction
NR = No Response

Categorize each response for erred items in Section 4 according to the following substitution categories.

Substitution Response Categories for Section 4:

SUPV = Superordinate Verb
COV = Coordinate Verb
SUBV = Subordinate Verb
CH = Chained
AV = Associated Verb
RN = Related Noun
PVA = Pro-Verbal Action
PAV = Phonemic Attribute of Verb
ISV = Initial Sound of Verb
VSV = Visual Substitution of Verb
VP = Visual Misperception
PWV = Part/Whole Verb
RWV = Root-Word Verb
IV = Innovative Verb
PL = Picture Labeling
CV = Circumlocution of Verb
SC = Substitution plus Self-Correction
NR = No Response

A substitution analysis might also be completed for a subject whose accuracy score is in the borderline range or whose overall comprehension score is low but who manifests word-finding difficulties on target words he or she knows. In this case, the substitution analysis should be conducted on only those words the person knew but could not name.

After recording the response codes for each section in the TAWF, tally the number of each substitution type across all five test sections, and enter the number of each response code in the spaces provided at the bottom of page 7 in the response booklet. Follow the same procedure in tallying the response codes for Section 4 and enter the totals at the bottom of page 7. Figure 3-12 presents

Section 1
Picture Naming: Nouns

Starter Items A. nose B. thumb C. kite D. whistle

Item	1 or 0		Subject's Response	Item Response Time			Ges. (✓)	Ex. Ver. (✓)	Comprehension		Response Code (after testing)
				☒ Estimated During Testing		☒ Actual from Tape Recording (sec/hun) (after testing)			Yes (✓)	No	
	Brief Test	Complete Test		Less Than 4 sec. (✓)	More Than 4 sec. (✓)						
1. ruler		1		✓		1 / 04					
2. mask		1			✓	4 / 16					
3. antenna		1		✓		1 / 90					
4. statue		0	man on a horse		✓	5 / 98			✓		C (VS)
5. crutch		1		✓		2 / 46					
6. suspenders		1		✓		2 / 16					
7. calculator		0	computer	✓		2 / 75			✓		CO
8. palm		1		✓		1 / 25					
9. microphone		1		✓		1 / 37					
10. dice		1		✓		1 / 36					
11. chopsticks		1		✓		3 / 35					
12. battery		0	box		✓	8 / 26			✓		VS
13. eyebrow		1		✓		1 / 25					
14. binoculars		1			✓	12 / 15	✓				
15. dart		1		✓		2 / 20					
16. magnet		1		✓		3 / 19					
17. acorn		0	fruit		✓	5 / 12			✓		CH
18. igloo		1		✓		1 / 42					
19. starfish		0	shellfish	✓		2 / 40			✓		PA
20. film		0	tape	✓		2 / 69			✓		VS
21. backpack		1		✓		2 / 49					
22. unicorn		1		✓		1 / 35					
23. harmonica		1		✓		2 / 46					
24. wishbone		0	I don't know		✓	15 / 80			✓		NR
25. propeller		1		✓		3 / 10					
26. jack		0	lifter		✓	6 / 59	✓		✓		FA
27. thimble		1		✓		2 / 16					
28. compass		0	directions	✓		2 / 42			✓		FA
29. funnel		0	siphon		✓	5 / 27			✓		CO
30. pliers		0	wrench	✓		1 / 88			✓		CO
31. dustpan		1		✓		2 / 86					
32. hopscotch		1		✓		1 / 88					
33. blimp		1			✓	4 / 78					
34. thermos		0	coffee cup	✓		2 / 28	✓		✓		PW
35. tambourine		0	drum	✓		2 / 20			✓		CO
36. spatula		1		✓		2 / 16	✓				
37. seahorse		0	dragon fish		✓	5 / 43			✓		VS

Brief Test Raw Score	RAW SCORE	Total Delayed Items	Total Item Response Time	Ges. Total	Ex. Ver. Total	Comprehension Total (total unknown)
	23	10	130/77	4	0	0

2

Figure 3-12. Coding responses for substitution types in Section 1 (response booklet, page 2).

Substitution Type Summary *(sections 1, 2, 3, and 5)*

Record from response code columns in sections 1, 2, 3, and 5, or use Appendix D, Figure D-1.

Type	Number	Type	Number	Type	Number
SUP		CH	1	PW	2
CO	4	PA	1	IN	
SUB		IS		GN	
FA	4	R	1	UN	
LA		AA		C	4
COM		VS	3	SC	
A	1	VP		NR	4

Substitution Type Summary *(section 4)*

Record from response code column in section 4, or use Appendix D, Figure D-2.

Type	Number	Type	Number	Type	Number
SUPV	1	CH		PWV	1
COV	3	PAV		PL	
SUBV		ISV		IV	
PVA		RWV		CV	
RN		VSV		SC	
AV	3	VP		NR	

7

Figure 3-13. Completed Substitution Type Summary (response booklet, page 7).

a sample of response coding in Section 1; Figure 3-13 shows a completed substitution-type summary.

After completing the analysis of substitution types, the TAWF *Response Booklet* should be completed. (The completed response booklet for Art, a sample subject, is provided in Appendix A.)

CHAPTER FOUR

INTERPRETATION OF THE TAWF RESULTS

FORMAL ANALYSES: ACCURACY AND TIME MEASUREMENT

An assessment of word-finding skills of adolescents and adults should incorporate information from several measurements that reflect different attributes of naming behavior. Important in the assessment of word finding in single-word naming are the following three indices: the accuracy index, the time index, and substitution types. These various measurements are included in the TAWF. Through both formal and informal analyses they can be used together in the assessment of an individual's word-finding skills. Following is a discussion of the scores resulting from each index along with guidelines for interpreting naming performance on the TAWF.

INTERPRETING ACCURACY RESULTS

Total Raw Score

The total raw score for accuracy is the number of correct responses on the TAWF. This score is calculated by summing the number of correct responses in each section and totaling these raw scores. In the formal analysis of an individual's word-finding skills, one should not interpret the raw scores within sections or across sections or use these scores alone. These scores are most meaningful when converted to standard scores or percentile ranks. In an informal analysis of an individual's word-finding skills, the examiner can compare an individual's raw scores for each section with the raw scores obtained by his or her grade- or age-level counterparts (See Tables E-1 and E-2 for mean raw scores of grade- and age-level groups for each TAWF section.)

Standard Score

The standard score is the most important score for determining a subject's naming accuracy on the TAWF. It was derived from raw-score transformations, resulting in a set of scores that have the same mean and standard deviation (Salvia & Ysseldyke, 1981) in each reference group. TAWF standard scores are defined by a mean of 100 and a standard deviation of 15. Using the procedures described in the TAWF *Technical Manual,* standard-score distributions were developed on the TAWF for age- and grade-level groupings. Use of the standard score allows the examiner to compare scores of specific subjects under study with the scores of subjects at the same grade or age level in the standardization sample. Norm Tables 1, 2, and 3 should be used to convert raw scores to standard scores based on individual grade and age distributions from the standardization sample.

In most cases TAWF examiners would use a standard score of 85 (−1 *SD*) as the appropriate cutoff score for determining accurate and inaccurate namers.

However, in some situations the characteristics of the local population differ from those of the nationally representative norming sample so greatly that the cutoff score of 85 may not be appropriate. For these situations a borderline range is provided for the accuracy standard score. This accuracy borderline range represents a confidence interval (based on 1 SEM, 68% confident) around the cutoff score of 85.

The borderline range may be used in two types of situations. First, there may be locales where the population differs from that of a nationally representative norming sample so greatly that the cutoff score of 85 would classify unusually small proportions of subjects in the inaccurate category. Here examiners may want to apply a broader interpretation and consider the upper bound of the borderline range (standard score of 90) as the cutoff between inaccurate and accurate namers. In these locales, subjects whose accuracy scores fall in the borderline range (86–90) would be considered borderline inaccurate, and examiners would want to follow up with observations of their retrieval skills in other situations in order to clarify their retrieval accuracy. Second, there may be other populations where representative national norms would classify unacceptably large proportions of subjects in the inaccurate category. In these locales, examiners may want to consider the lower bound of the borderline range as the cutoff score (80).

Percentile Rank

Percentile ranks are *derived scores* that reflect the percentage of scores in the sample that occurred at or below a specified raw score (Salvia & Ysseldyke, 1981). That is, an eighth-grade student receiving a TAWF score at the 80th percentile obtained a score that was equal to or greater than the scores obtained by 80% of the standardization sample in the same grade. Percentiles were computed for each grade and age level. Norm Table 5 presents the percentile rank for adolescents for each TAWF Total Raw Score by age level; Norm Table 6 presents the percentile rank for adolescents for each TAWF Total Raw Score by grade level; and Norm Table 7 presents the percentile rank for each TAWF Total Raw Score for the adults in the standardization sample.

Accuracy Profiles

After obtaining the standard score for a particular subject, an examiner may want to compare the score of the subject under study with the mean standard score achieved by subjects in the same grade or age grouping in the standardization sample. Such comparisons can result in profiles that describe a subject's strengths and weaknesses when naming in constrained naming tasks. Based on descriptive categories typically assigned to interpretation of standard scores, a subject's word-finding behavior can be classified as inaccurate or accurate naming. The examiner should classify the subject under study according to one of these groupings in order to determine if his or her difficulties in finding words manifest themselves in inaccurate responses. Adolescents or adults classified in the inaccurate naming category (inaccurate namers) are those whose accuracy score falls below one standard deviation from the mean of the normal subjects in the standardization sample (i.e., below 85). Individuals classified as *inaccurate namers* are considered to demonstrate below average word-finding skills on the TAWF with respect to accuracy.

To illustrate the interpretation of standard scores, a sample case follows. Geoff, an eighth grader, was referred to the speech and language pathologist because "although he knows the right answer, he often has difficulty answering questions in class or finding the right words to express himself." Geoff's word-finding skills were assessed on the TAWF. With respect to accuracy, he received a raw score of 76 and a standard score of 79, placing him in the sixth percentile compared to his grade mates. Geoff's comprehension of the target words on all the items he missed was checked. Receptively, he indicated that he knew the erred items (receiving a "high" on comprehension summary). Geoff's accuracy score is more than one standard deviation below the mean of his grade mates in the presence of good comprehension of the target words he missed. Thus, his score falls in the inaccurate naming category range. The accuracy index was sensitive in assessing Geoff's naming behavior in that, when Geoff was having difficulty finding words, he either produced an incorrect response or no response, resulting in a low TAWF accuracy score. It appears that Geoff may have some word-finding difficulties that manifest themselves in many inaccuracies. In the following discussion, we will look at Geoff's performance with respect to the other indices used to assess word finding. Figure 4-1 displays Geoff's accuracy results.

INTERPRETING TIME MEASUREMENT AND PROCEDURES

A second index that is useful in the assessment of word-finding skills is the measurement of the time subjects take to name the TAWF pictures. Two response-time evaluations are provided for the analysis of latencies on the TAWF: (1) the Estimated Item Response Time procedure, and (2) the optional Actual Item Response Time measurement. Either or both of these assessments may be completed.

Estimated Item Response Time Procedure

The Estimated Item Response Time (ERT) procedure is a procedure used to judge the amount of time it takes an individual to name a target word in Section 1, Picture Naming: Nouns. After judging the naming speed of each target word in Section 1, the examiner compares the number of delayed responses (4 seconds or longer) to the grade- or age-level standard for the individual under study. Of interest is how the individual compares with his or her grade- or age-level counterparts. For example, if a subject produced a number of delayed responses (4 seconds or longer) equal to or greater than the grade- or age-level

NATIONAL COLLEGE OF EDUCATION

RESPONSE BOOKLET

TEST OF ADOLESCENT/ADULT WORD FINDING

TAWF

Diane J. German, Ph.D.

Name Geoff

School ______ Grade 8

Examiner ______

Teacher ______

Referred by ______

Address ______

______ Phone ______

Parent/Guardian/Spouse/Caretaker ______

	Year	Month	Day
Test Date	89	1	10
(−) Birthdate	76	1	5
(=) Age	13	0	5*

*If the number of days exceeds 15, add a month to the age.

☐ Brief Test

☒ Complete Test

If following up the Brief Test with the complete test, record the complete test results in a different color.

Accuracy Score Summary

Section	Raw Score: Brief Test	Raw Score: Complete Test
1. Picture Naming: Nouns		23
2. Sentence Completion Naming		12
3. Description Naming		9
4. Picture Naming: Verbs		17
5. Category Naming		15
TOTAL RAW SCORE		76

Scores Based on ☐ Age ☒ Grade

	Brief Test	Complete Test
Standard Score (SS)	(Table 5-1, 5-2, or 5-3)	79 (Norm Table 1, 2, or 3)
Standard Error of Measurement (SEM)	(Table 5-1, 5-2, or 5-3)	4.42 (Norm Table 1, 2, or 3)
Range of Confidence (SS − 1 and + 1 SEM)	___ to ___	75 to 83
Percentile Rank	(Table 5-5, 5-6, or 5-7)	6 (Norm Table 5, 6, or 7)

Plot the SS on the Word Finding Profile *(page 8)*.

Comprehension Summary *(from page 7)*

HIGH ☒ Percent of comprehension is high.

LOW ☐ Percent of comprehension is low. *(Refer to Prorated Accuracy Rescoring Procedure on page 7.)*

Item Response Time Summary *(Section 1, Picture Naming: Nouns)*

Estimated Item Response Time (ERT) (Number of Delayed Responses — 4 Seconds or More), Brief Test = ______

Estimated Item Response Time (ERT) (Number of Delayed Responses — 4 Seconds or More), Complete Test = ______

Total Item Response Time, Complete Test = ___/___ in seconds/hundredths

Average Item Response Time (ART), Complete Test = Total Item Response Time/37 = ___/___ in seconds/hundredths

Plot the ERT or the ART on the Word Finding Profile *(page 8)*.

Word Finding Profile

Profile A: ☐ Fast and inaccurate namer

Profile B: ☐ Slow and inaccurate namer

Profile C: ☐ Fast and accurate namer

Profile D: ☐ Slow and accurate namer

DLM
One DLM Park • Allen, Texas 75002

1

Figure 4-1. Geoff's comprehension and accuracy results on the TAWF (response booklet, page 1).

standard, the subject would be considered a Slow Namer. However, if he or she produced fewer delayed responses (4 seconds or longer), he or she would be considered a Fast Namer. Grade- and age-level standards for the Estimated Item Response Time procedure are presented in Appendix F.

Actual Item Response Time Measurement (Optional)

The second, more precise evaluation of naming latencies is the actual Average Item Response Time (ART) evaluation. In this analysis the examiner measures the time it took the subject to name each individual picture in Section 1. (This procedure is described in Chapter 3.) These actual item response times are summed to produce the Total Item Response Time. To determine the Average Item Response Time (ART), the examiner should divide the Total Item Response Time by 37 (number of items in Section 1), as indicated on the cover of the response booklet. After calculating the ART for Section 1, compare the results with the means and standard deviations of the adolescent's grade- or age-level peers or the adult's age-level peers in the standardization sample (the Grade-Level or Age Grouping Standards) presented in Appendix F. For example, a student whose ART is equal to or greater than the grade-level standard would be assessed as manifesting a significantly slow Average Item Response Time (ART).

Borderline ranges are provided for both the Estimated Item Response Time and the Average Item Response Time cutoff scores differentiating Slow and Fast Namers. These item response time borderline ranges represent the range of confidence (based on 1 SEM, 68% confident) of the item response time cutoff (+1 *SD*). In most cases examiners would use the grade- or age-level standard as the appropriate cutoff for determining Slow and Fast Namers. However, in some situations the characteristics of the local population differ from those of the nationally representative norming sample so greatly that the grade- or age-level standard would classify unusually small proportions of subjects in the Slow category. In these locales, examiners may want to apply a broader interpretation and consider the lower bound of the borderline range as the cutoff between Slow and Fast Namers. Subjects whose time scores (ERT or ART) fall in the borderline range would be considered borderline Slow, and examiners would want to follow up with observations of their retrieval skills in other situations in order to clarify their retrieval speed. Similarly, in other situations where representative national norms would classify unacceptably large proportions of subjects in the Slow category, examiners may want to consider the upper bound of the borderline range as the cutoff.

Time-Measurement Profiles

When analyzing word-finding skills with respect to speed of naming, individuals can be classified into two categories, Slow Namers and Fast Namers. The examiner can use either the Estimated Item Response Time procedure, the optional Actual Item Response Time measurement, or both to classify individuals under study. With ERT, an individual who has the same number of, or a greater number of, delayed responses (4 seconds or longer) than the grade- or age-level standard would be a Slow Namer. An individual who has fewer delayed responses than the grade- or age-level standard would be a Fast Namer.

With the Actual Item Response Time measurement, Slow Namers are those individuals whose Average Item Response Time is at or above the grade- or age-level standard, described above. (If the examiner considers the borderline ranges, subjects whose time scores fall in the borderline range would be considered borderline Slow Namers.) Fast Namers are those individuals whose Average Item Response Time is faster than the grade- or age-level standard (or the lower bound of the borderline range in cases where the borderline range is used).

To illustrate the use of the time index, we will continue our analysis of Geoff's word-finding skills. For Geoff, the examiner completed the Actual Item Response Time measurement. Geoff's Average Item Response Time was 2.40 seconds, slower than the grade-level standard (2.22 seconds). These findings indicate that Geoff's naming performance on the TAWF was slower than these grade-level standards. He would, therefore, be classified as a Slow Namer. Figure 4-2 presents results of time analyses for Geoff.

ACCURACY AND TIME PROFILES

The TAWF accuracy and time indices can be used together to establish profiles of word-finding skills. A subject's naming performance can be classified into one of four accuracy and time categories: *Profile A, Fast and Inaccurate Namers; Profile B, Slow and Inaccurate Namers; Profile C, Fast and Accurate Namers;* and *Profile D, Slow and Accurate Namers.* The Word Finding Profile on page 8 of the response booklet clearly displays these four naming profiles and the

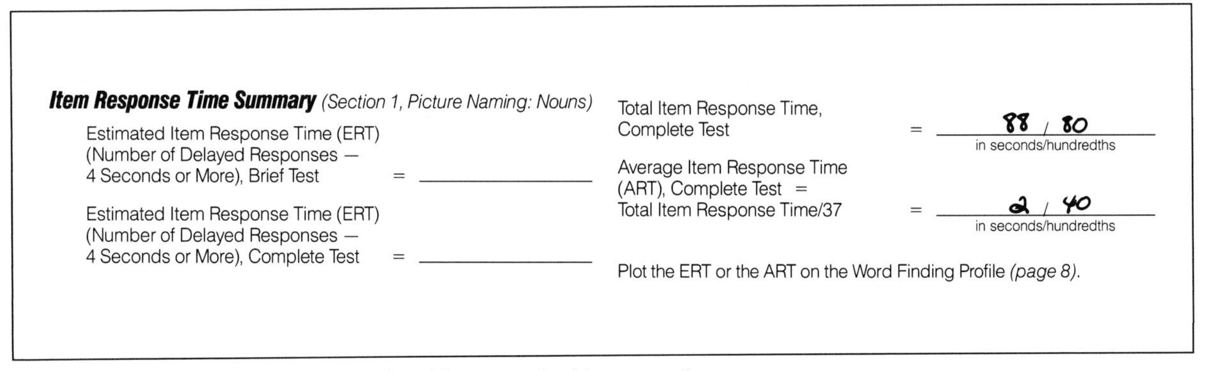

Item Response Time Summary *(Section 1, Picture Naming: Nouns)*

Estimated Item Response Time (ERT) (Number of Delayed Responses — 4 Seconds or More), Brief Test = ______

Estimated Item Response Time (ERT) (Number of Delayed Responses — 4 Seconds or More), Complete Test = ______

Total Item Response Time, Complete Test = 88 / 80 (in seconds/hundredths)

Average Item Response Time (ART), Complete Test = Total Item Response Time/37 = 2 / 40 (in seconds/hundredths)

Plot the ERT or the ART on the Word Finding Profile *(page 8).*

Figure 4-2. Results of time analyses for Geoff (response booklet, page 1).

relationship between the time and accuracy indices. Following is a description of each of the four word-finding profiles.

Profile A: Fast and Inaccurate Namers

Individuals classified in the fast and inaccurate category earn the following scores:

1. Accuracy score is more than one standard deviation below the mean of their peers in the standardization sample (below 85) or below the borderline range cutoff score (e.g., 80 or 90).
2. The number of delayed responses (4 seconds or longer) is less than the grade- or age-level standard.

or

3. The ART is less than the grade- or age-level standard.

These individuals are not slow in naming, but they are often inaccurate.

Profile B: Slow and Inaccurate Namers

Individuals who fall into the slow and inaccurate category earn the following scores:

1. Accuracy score is more than one standard deviation below the mean of their peers in the standardization sample (below 85) or below the borderline range cutoff score (e.g., 80 or 90).
2. The number of delayed responses (4 seconds or longer) is the same as or greater than the grade- or age-level standard (or in the borderline range).

or

3. The ART is the same as or greater than the grade- or age-level standard (or in the borderline range).

These individuals manifest problems in both naming speed and naming accuracy and are the individuals most often identified as having word-finding problems.

Profile C: Fast and Accurate Namers

Individuals classified as fast and accurate namers are those who earn the following scores:

1. Accuracy score is less than one standard deviation below the mean of their peers in the standardization sample (above 85) or above the borderline range cutoff score (e.g., 80 or 90).
2. The number of delayed responses (4 seconds or longer) is less than the grade- or age-level standard.

or

3. The ART is less than the grade- or age-level standard.

The profile of fast and accurate namers does not indicate accuracy or latency problems when naming. This profile represents those individuals who have not manifested word-finding difficulties on the TAWF.

Profile D: Slow and Accurate Namers

Individuals classified within the last profile, Slow and Accurate Namers, earn the following scores:

1. Accuracy score is less than one standard deviation below the mean of their peers in the standardization sample (above 85) or above the borderline range cutoff score (e.g., 80 or 90).
2. The number of delayed responses (4 seconds or longer) is equal to or greater than the grade- or age-level standard (or in the borderline range).

or

3. The ART is equal to or greater than the grade- or age-level standard (or in the borderline range).

Although these individuals are Slow Namers, they are accurate. As a result, they are often not identified as demonstrating word-finding difficulties.

Sample Profiles

To illustrate the usefulness of the TAWF naming profiles, let us look at Geoff's performance on the TAWF. Plotting his performance on the Word Finding Profile (see Figure 4-3) indicates that Geoff earned an accuracy score that was more than one standard deviation below the mean of the normally learning students in the standardization sample. In addition, his responses were slower than expected, as his ART was more than one standard deviation above the mean of his grade mates (above the grade-level standard). When plotted, Geoff's scores fall in the profile chart quadrant labeled *slow and inaccurate* (see Figure 4-3). Based on these findings, Geoff would be classified as both a slow and inaccurate namer. Therefore, in class or at home he might be expected to take longer to respond and may often give an incorrect response. He may appear not to know requested information which in reality he does know but has difficulty expressing.

Rose, a tenth grader identified as having word-finding problems, produced a different TAWF profile (see Figure 4-4). She was referred to the speech and language pathologist for an evaluation and was described by her classroom teacher as a student who "often quickly verbalizes the wrong word when a specific response is requested, but immediately self-corrects." Rose's TAWF accuracy score consisted of a raw score of 79 with a standard score of 77, placing her at the fifth percentile when compared to other tenth graders. Her comprehension score, however, was in the 95 to 100% range, indicating that she knew the target words she had difficulty naming. Although Rose's accuracy score was more than one standard deviation below the mean, her time measurements fell in the fast range. Her Average Item Response Time was 1.55 seconds, faster than the grade-level standard (2.11 seconds). Rose's accuracy score and item response-time index are plotted on the Word Finding Profile in Figure 4-4. As illustrated, her scores fall in the profile chart quadrant labeled *fast and inaccurate.* Based on these results, Rose is classified as a fast

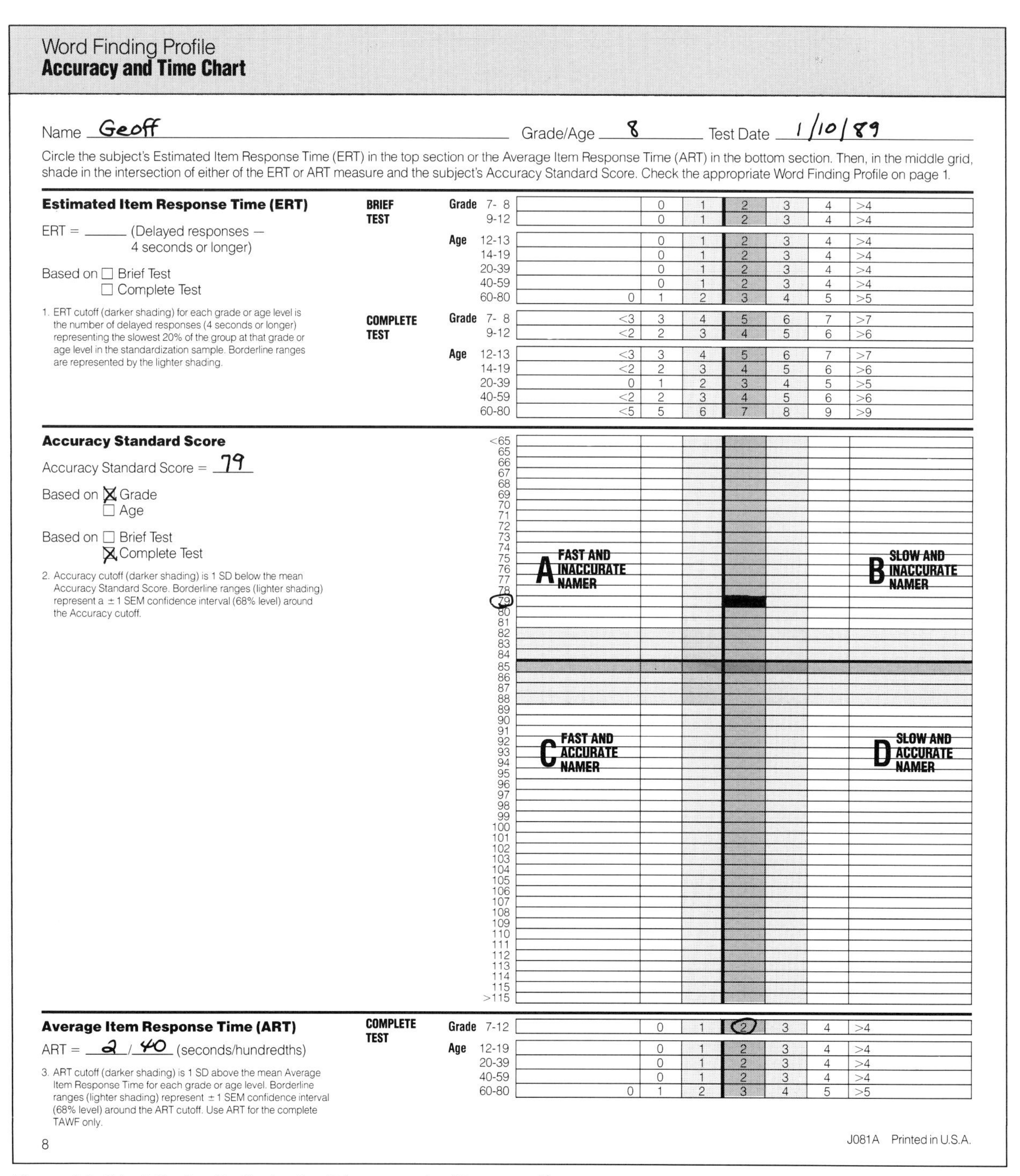

Word Finding Profile
Accuracy and Time Chart

Name Geoff Grade/Age 8 Test Date 1/10/89

Circle the subject's Estimated Item Response Time (ERT) in the top section or the Average Item Response Time (ART) in the bottom section. Then, in the middle grid, shade in the intersection of either of the ERT or ART measure and the subject's Accuracy Standard Score. Check the appropriate Word Finding Profile on page 1.

Estimated Item Response Time (ERT)

ERT = ______ (Delayed responses — 4 seconds or longer)

Based on ☐ Brief Test
☐ Complete Test

1. ERT cutoff (darker shading) for each grade or age level is the number of delayed responses (4 seconds or longer) representing the slowest 20% of the group at that grade or age level in the standardization sample. Borderline ranges are represented by the lighter shading.

Test		Level							
BRIEF TEST	Grade	7- 8		0	1	2	3	4	>4
		9-12		0	1	2	3	4	>4
	Age	12-13		0	1	2	3	4	>4
		14-19		0	1	2	3	4	>4
		20-39		0	1	2	3	4	>4
		40-59		0	1	2	3	4	>4
		60-80	0	1	2	3	4	5	>5
COMPLETE TEST	Grade	7- 8	<3	3	4	5	6	7	>7
		9-12	<2	2	3	4	5	6	>6
	Age	12-13	<3	3	4	5	6	7	>7
		14-19	<2	2	3	4	5	6	>6
		20-39	0	1	2	3	4	5	>5
		40-59	<2	2	3	4	5	6	>6
		60-80	<5	5	6	7	8	9	>9

Accuracy Standard Score

Accuracy Standard Score = 79

Based on ☒ Grade
☐ Age

Based on ☐ Brief Test
☒ Complete Test

2. Accuracy cutoff (darker shading) is 1 SD below the mean Accuracy Standard Score. Borderline ranges (lighter shading) represent a ± 1 SEM confidence interval (68% level) around the Accuracy cutoff.

<65, 65, 66, 67, 68, 69, 70, 71, 72, 73, 74, 75, 76, 77, 78, 79, 80, 81, 82, 83, 84, 85, 86, 87, 88, 89, 90, 91, 92, 93, 94, 95, 96, 97, 98, 99, 100, 101, 102, 103, 104, 105, 106, 107, 108, 109, 110, 111, 112, 113, 114, 115, >115

A FAST AND INACCURATE NAMER

B SLOW AND INACCURATE NAMER

C FAST AND ACCURATE NAMER

D SLOW AND ACCURATE NAMER

Average Item Response Time (ART)

ART = 2 / 40 (seconds/hundredths)

3. ART cutoff (darker shading) is 1 SD above the mean Average Item Response Time for each grade or age level. Borderline ranges (lighter shading) represent ± 1 SEM confidence interval (68% level) around the ART cutoff. Use ART for the complete TAWF only.

Test		Level							
COMPLETE TEST	Grade	7-12		0	1	2	3	4	>4
	Age	12-19		0	1	2	3	4	>4
		20-39		0	1	2	3	4	>4
		40-59		0	1	2	3	4	>4
		60-80	0	1	2	3	4	5	>5

8

J081A Printed in U.S.A.

Figure 4-3. Word Finding Profile for Geoff (response booklet, page 8).

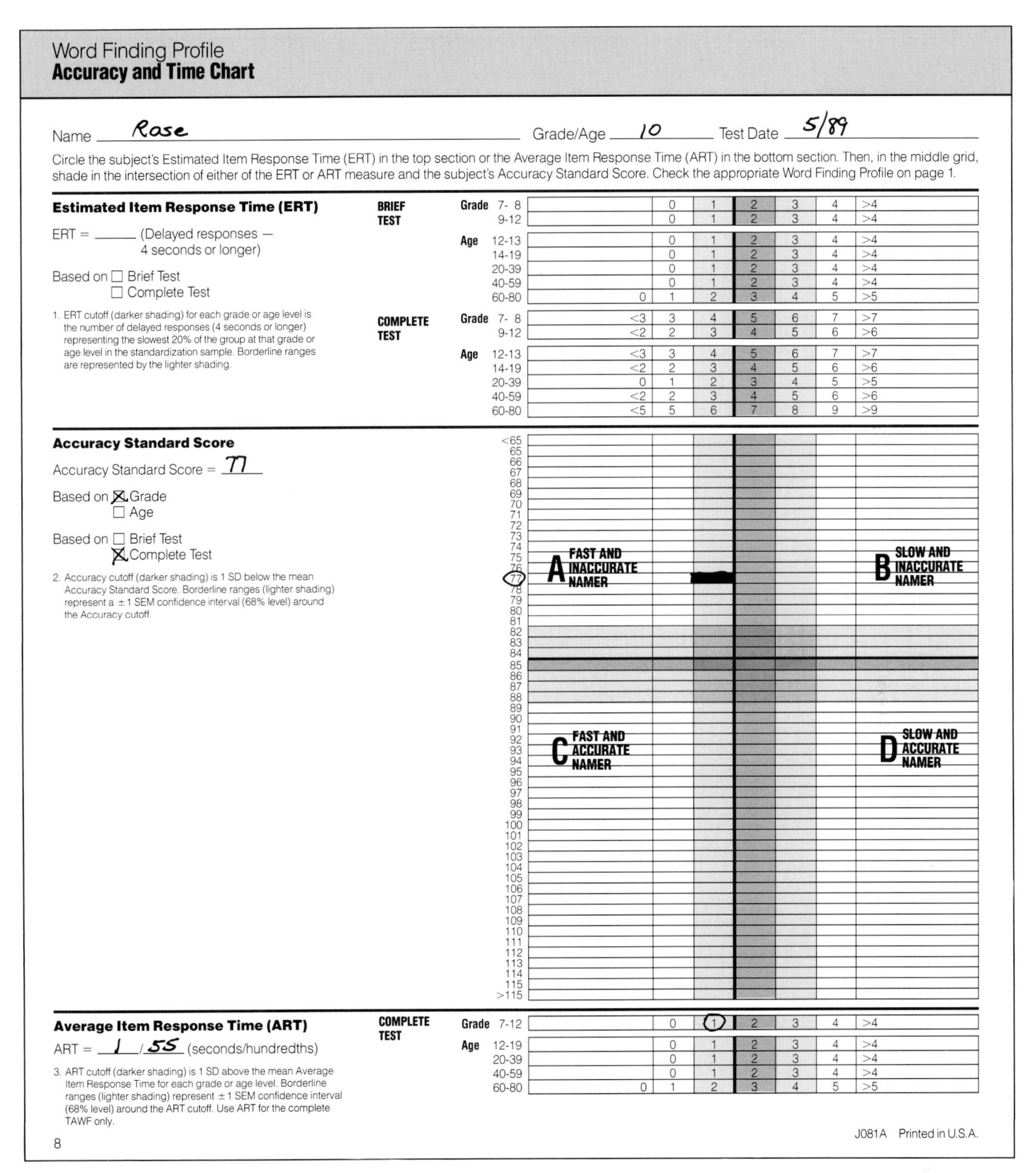

Word Finding Profile
Accuracy and Time Chart

Name Rose Grade/Age 10 Test Date 5/89

Circle the subject's Estimated Item Response Time (ERT) in the top section or the Average Item Response Time (ART) in the bottom section. Then, in the middle grid, shade in the intersection of either of the ERT or ART measure and the subject's Accuracy Standard Score. Check the appropriate Word Finding Profile on page 1.

Estimated Item Response Time (ERT)

ERT = ______ (Delayed responses — 4 seconds or longer)

Based on ☐ Brief Test
☐ Complete Test

1. ERT cutoff (darker shading) for each grade or age level is the number of delayed responses (4 seconds or longer) representing the slowest 20% of the group at that grade or age level in the standardization sample. Borderline ranges are represented by the lighter shading.

Test		Level							
BRIEF TEST	Grade	7- 8		0	1	2	3	4	>4
		9-12		0	1	2	3	4	>4
	Age	12-13		0	1	2	3	4	>4
		14-19		0	1	2	3	4	>4
		20-39		0	1	2	3	4	>4
		40-59		0	1	2	3	4	>4
		60-80	0	1	2	3	4	5	>5
COMPLETE TEST	Grade	7- 8	<3	3	4	5	6	7	>7
		9-12	<2	2	3	4	5	6	>6
	Age	12-13	<3	3	4	5	6	7	>7
		14-19	<2	2	3	4	5	6	>6
		20-39	0	1	2	3	4	5	>5
		40-59	<2	2	3	4	5	6	>6
		60-80	<5	5	6	7	8	9	>9

Accuracy Standard Score

Accuracy Standard Score = 77

Based on ☒ Grade
☐ Age

Based on ☐ Brief Test
☒ Complete Test

2. Accuracy cutoff (darker shading) is 1 SD below the mean Accuracy Standard Score. Borderline ranges (lighter shading) represent a ± 1 SEM confidence interval (68% level) around the Accuracy cutoff.

<65 65 66 67 68 69 70 71 72 73 74 75 76 77 78 79 80 81 82 83 84 85 86 87 88 89 90 91 92 93 94 95 96 97 98 99 100 101 102 103 104 105 106 107 108 109 110 111 112 113 114 115 >115

A FAST AND INACCURATE NAMER

B SLOW AND INACCURATE NAMER

C FAST AND ACCURATE NAMER

D SLOW AND ACCURATE NAMER

Average Item Response Time (ART)

ART = 1 / 55 (seconds/hundredths)

3. ART cutoff (darker shading) is 1 SD above the mean Average Item Response Time for each grade or age level. Borderline ranges (lighter shading) represent ± 1 SEM confidence interval (68% level) around the ART cutoff. Use ART for the complete TAWF only.

Test		Level							
COMPLETE TEST	Grade	7-12		0	1	2	3	4	>4
	Age	12-19		0	1	2	3	4	>4
		20-39		0	1	2	3	4	>4
		40-59		0	1	2	3	4	>4
		60-80	0	1	2	3	4	5	>5

8

J081A Printed in U.S.A.

Figure 4-4. Word Finding Profile for Rose (response booklet, page 8).

but inaccurate namer. She could, therefore, be expected to respond quickly in the classroom or at home, but often inaccurately. As the referring teacher initially indicated, Rose often self-corrects her word-finding errors immediately. This behavior was also observed in her performance on the TAWF, where she would name a picture incorrectly and then quickly give the target word. Although Rose's self-corrections signal that she knows the word, her first response was incorrect and was therefore counted as a word-finding error. (In word-finding assessment it is always the first response that is scored.)

In contrast to Rose and Geoff is a ninth grader named Leo. Leo has been described as a very slow but accurate responder in the classroom. When called upon to respond, he often looks blank before attempting to answer. However, his teacher reports that if she waits, he will verbalize the correct response. Leo was administered the TAWF and received an accuracy raw score of 99 and a standard score of 110, placing him in the seventy-fifth percentile. With respect to accuracy, Leo was in the average range. However, his time scores fell in the slow range. His Average Item Response Time was 3.00 seconds, slower than the grade-level standard (2.06 seconds). As a result, Leo would be classified as a slow but accurate namer on the TAWF (see Figure 4-5). He is a student who may not respond immediately when called on in class, but if given time will usually verbalize the correct answer.

INFORMAL ANALYSES

COMPREHENSION ASSESSMENT

Differential diagnosis of receptive versus expressive language problems is critical in the assessment of word-finding skills. By definition, an individual with word-finding problems has difficulty finding words in the presence of good comprehension of those same words. However, individuals with problems in understanding language may also appear to have word-finding problems. Their difficulties in expressive language stem from underlying comprehension problems with the very vocabulary they have difficulty naming. In order to differentiate receptive from expressive language problems in the individual under study, the individual's comprehension of the target words missed on the TAWF should be assessed.

Although the TAWF is not a receptive language assessment measure, it provides a comprehension section to help the examiner determine whether an individual knows the target words missed during the naming assessment. Thus, target-word comprehension should be checked for each TAWF item a subject misses. The examiner should calculate the percentage of items the individual understood on the TAWF by subtracting the number of unknown words (words the individual did not pass in the comprehension check) from the total number of items administered (107) and then divide by the total number of items admin-

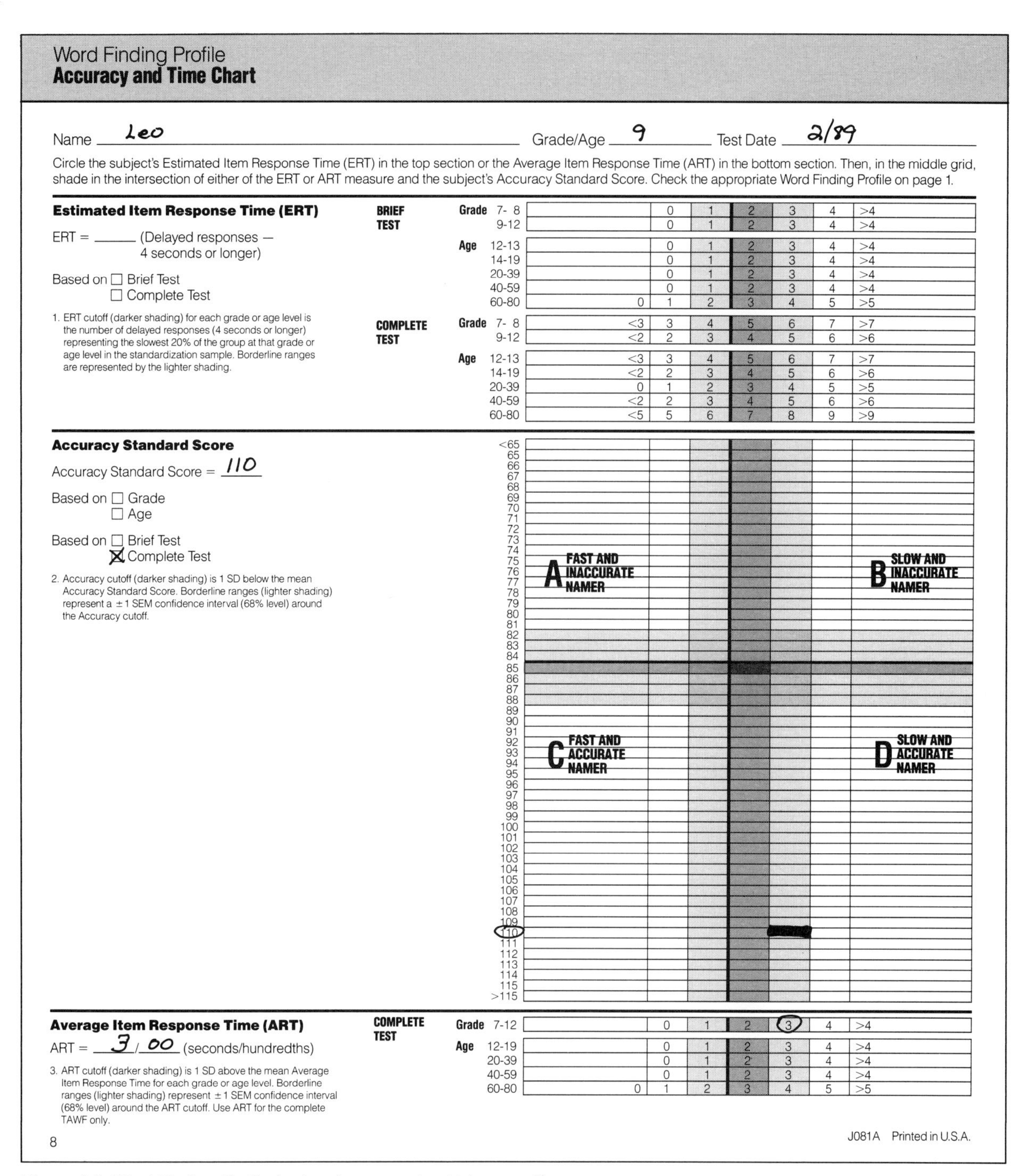

Word Finding Profile
Accuracy and Time Chart

Name Leo Grade/Age 9 Test Date 2/89

Circle the subject's Estimated Item Response Time (ERT) in the top section or the Average Item Response Time (ART) in the bottom section. Then, in the middle grid, shade in the intersection of either of the ERT or ART measure and the subject's Accuracy Standard Score. Check the appropriate Word Finding Profile on page 1.

Estimated Item Response Time (ERT)

ERT = ______ (Delayed responses — 4 seconds or longer)

Based on ☐ Brief Test
☐ Complete Test

1. ERT cutoff (darker shading) for each grade or age level is the number of delayed responses (4 seconds or longer) representing the slowest 20% of the group at that grade or age level in the standardization sample. Borderline ranges are represented by the lighter shading.

Test		Level								
BRIEF TEST	Grade	7- 8			0	1	2	3	4	>4
		9-12			0	1	2	3	4	>4
	Age	12-13			0	1	2	3	4	>4
		14-19			0	1	2	3	4	>4
		20-39			0	1	2	3	4	>4
		40-59			0	1	2	3	4	>4
		60-80		0	1	2	3	4	5	>5
COMPLETE TEST	Grade	7- 8		<3	3	4	5	6	7	>7
		9-12		<2	2	3	4	5	6	>6
	Age	12-13		<3	3	4	5	6	7	>7
		14-19		<2	2	3	4	5	6	>6
		20-39		0	1	2	3	4	5	>5
		40-59		<2	2	3	4	5	6	>6
		60-80		<5	5	6	7	8	9	>9

Accuracy Standard Score

Accuracy Standard Score = 110

Based on ☐ Grade
☐ Age

Based on ☐ Brief Test
☒ Complete Test

2. Accuracy cutoff (darker shading) is 1 SD below the mean Accuracy Standard Score. Borderline ranges (lighter shading) represent a ± 1 SEM confidence interval (68% level) around the Accuracy cutoff.

<65, 65, 66, 67, 68, 69, 70, 71, 72, 73, 74, 75, 76, 77, 78, 79, 80, 81, 82, 83, 84, 85, 86, 87, 88, 89, 90, 91, 92, 93, 94, 95, 96, 97, 98, 99, 100, 101, 102, 103, 104, 105, 106, 107, 108, 109, 110, 111, 112, 113, 114, 115, >115

A FAST AND INACCURATE NAMER

B SLOW AND INACCURATE NAMER

C FAST AND ACCURATE NAMER

D SLOW AND ACCURATE NAMER

Average Item Response Time (ART)

ART = 3 / 00 (seconds/hundredths)

3. ART cutoff (darker shading) is 1 SD above the mean Average Item Response Time for each grade or age level. Borderline ranges (lighter shading) represent ± 1 SEM confidence interval (68% level) around the ART cutoff. Use ART for the complete TAWF only.

Test		Level								
COMPLETE TEST	Grade	7-12			0	1	2	3	4	>4
	Age	12-19			0	1	2	3	4	>4
		20-39			0	1	2	3	4	>4
		40-59			0	1	2	3	4	>4
		60-80		0	1	2	3	4	5	>5

8

J081A Printed in U.S.A.

Figure 4-5. Word Finding Profile for Leo (response booklet, page 8).

istered (as indicated in the response booklet, page 7). In the TAWF *Technical Manual,* Appendix A presents the percentages of normal individuals in the standardization sample comprehending each item. These percentages ranged from 95% to 100% for all TAWF target words, with the majority of words comprehended by 100% of the sample. The mean comprehension percentage for the entire standardization sample on the TAWF items was 99%. Based on these findings, a conservative criterion for diagnosing word-finding problems on the TAWF requires that an individual indicate at least 95% comprehension of the words administered (102 words comprehended). A more liberal interpretation allows a comprehension criterion score of 90% (96 items comprehended). It is recommended that the clinician apply at least a 90% criterion in deciding whether the individual under study has a low or high comprehension score on the TAWF. A comprehension percentage below 90% should be viewed as a low score on the TAWF and should signal the need to conduct the Prorated Accuracy Rescoring procedure for low comprehension (presented in Chapter 3 and discussed below). It may be that what first appeared to be a word-finding problem is in reality a lack of knowledge of the TAWF target words.

Prorated Accuracy Rescoring Procedure for Low Comprehension

Professionals have identified three types of individuals who manifest problems in finding words.

1. Type 1. These individuals have word-finding difficulties in the presence of good understanding of language (this is the classical definition of word-finding disorders). Thus they have difficulty retrieving words that they know. Identification of these subjects on the TAWF is straightforward as they will receive comprehension scores of 90 to 100% on the TAWF comprehension assessment and TAWF accuracy scores below 85 (or within or below the borderline range of 80–90). The examiner need not use the Prorated Accuracy Rescoring procedure with these individuals. Their comprehension scores on the TAWF are high, and one would not suspect underlying problems in understanding language. These subjects' accuracy scores reflect their expressive word-finding skills. If their standard score is below 85 (or in the borderline range of 80–90), one would identify them as Inaccurate Namers.
2. Type 2. These subjects have problems understanding language and manifest word-finding difficulties on words they do not know or that are not stable in their receptive language. They do not manifest word-finding difficulties on words they know (thus they have underlying comprehension problems).
3. Type 3. These are dually handicapped subjects; they have problems both in understanding language and in word finding. That is, the subjects have difficulty finding words they don't know (underlying comprehension problems) and also manifest word-finding problems on words they do know (underlying expressive language word-finding problems).

Differentiating among these three types of individuals is challenging. The Prorated Accuracy Rescoring procedure explained in Chapter 3 is recommended to help differentiate among these individuals.

If, after applying the Prorated Accuracy Rescoring procedure, you find that a particular student's prorated standard score is above 85 (or above the 80 to 90 borderline range), you would conclude that this individual's naming errors are only on words that he or she does not know. This finding would be typical of Type 2 above, suggesting that a problem in understanding language is causing difficulty in finding words. This would not be a true expressive language word-finding deficit, because on words the individual knows he or she does not have a word-finding deficit. Further assessment in language comprehension would be needed to clarify the individual's understanding of language.

However, if you find that the prorated standard score after rescoring is still below 85 (or in the 80 to 90 borderline range), you might suspect that this individual is Type 3, exhibiting the dual handicaps of problems in understanding language and an expressive word-finding disorder. You would conclude that this individual has word-finding problems on words that he or she knows and may also have problems understanding language. Further assessment in language comprehension would be needed to clarify this individual's comprehension skills.

As indicated above, this Prorated Accuracy Rescoring procedure is appropriate for individuals who do not meet the comprehension criterion for the TAWF. It would be appropriate for individuals you suspect may have problems in understanding language but whose expressive language word-finding skills are unclear. It would also be appropriate for bilingual subjects whom you know have low receptive vocabulary skills in standard English, but whose expressive language word-finding skills on known vocabulary are unclear.

To illustrate the usefulness of the Prorated Accuracy Rescoring procedure, let's look at Joe's performance on the TAWF. Joe is an eleventh grader who earned an accuracy score more than one standard deviation below the mean of the normally learning students in the standardization sample (raw score = 83, standard score =80). In addition, his responses were slower than expected, as his Average Item Response Time (ART) was slower than the grade-level standard for eleventh graders (i.e., 3.00 seconds compared to the grade-level standard of 1.99). When plotted, Joe's scores indicated that he was a slow and inaccurate namer. In addition, Joe's comprehension score was 84% (he missed 17 items on the comprehension assessment), which is considered low comprehension on the TAWF. Thus, any interpretation of Joe's accuracy score must consider whether he even knows the words he is unable to name. The challenge now is to determine if Joe has a problem in understanding language as well as a word-finding disorder or if his word-finding difficulties are symptomatic of underlying language comprehension deficits. The examiner employed the Prorated Accuracy Rescoring procedure for low comprehension and rescored Joe's response booklet. She then calculated the Prorated Accuracy Raw Score and used it to find his Prorated Accuracy Standard Score in the appropriate norm table. Joe's new raw score was 98 (83 [raw score from Accuracy Score Summary] ÷ 90 [known words from Comprehension Summary] = 92% of known words named correctly; 92% of 107 items administered = 98), which is equivalent to a standard score of 105. Joe's accuracy score is now above the grade-level standard of 85. Because this new accuracy score represents naming errors on words that Joe knows, it suggests that Joe does not have significant word-finding difficulties on words he knows. He thus does not fit the classical definition of having a word-finding disorder; rather, he may have underlying problems in understanding language (Type 2). That is, Joe manifested naming difficulties only on words he did not know and did not manifest significant naming difficulties on words he knew on the TAWF. Follow-up receptive language testing would be needed to clarify Joe's language comprehension skills. The Prorated Accuracy Rescoring procedure helped the examiner complete a differential diagnosis to help determine Joe's underlying language difficulties.

A second student who received a low comprehension score on the TAWF was Mary. Mary is a twelfth grader who earned an accuracy score more than one standard deviation below the mean of the normally learning students in the standardization sample (raw score = 70, standard score = 61). In addition, her responses were slower than expected, as her Average Item Response Time was slower than the grade-level standard (ART = 3.25 seconds) for grade 12. When plotted, Mary's scores indicated that she was a slow and inaccurate namer. In addition, Mary's comprehension score was 86% (she missed 15 items in the comprehension assessment), which is considered low. Thus, the interpretation of Mary's accuracy score must consider whether she even knows the words she is unable to name. The challenge now is to determine if Mary has a problem in receptive language as well as a word-finding disorder or if she has problems only in understanding language. The examiner employed the Prorated Accuracy Rescoring procedure for low comprehension with Mary also. She rescored Mary's response booklet and then calculated the Prorated Accuracy Raw Score and used it to find her Prorated Accuracy Standard Score in the appropriate norm table. Mary's prorated raw score was 81 (70 [raw score from Accuracy Score Summary] ÷ 92 [known words from Comprehension Summary] = 76% of known words named correctly; 76% of 107 items administered = 81), which is equivalent to a standard score of 71, below the grade-level standard and the 80 to 90 borderline range. Because this prorated standard score represents naming errors on words that Mary knows, it suggests that Mary does have significant word-finding difficulties on words she knows. She thus may be a dually handicapped student with word-finding disorders as well as a problem in understanding language (Type 3). That is, Mary manifested naming difficulties on words she knew as well as a low comprehension score on the TAWF. Follow-up testing of her receptive language would be needed to clarify Mary's language comprehension skills. The Prorated Accuracy Rescoring procedure helped the examiner complete a differential diagnosis to help determine Mary's underlying language difficulties.

RESPONSE ANALYSIS

A second informal evaluation that is useful in identifying individuals with word-finding problems is an analysis of the types of substitutions they manifest when they experience difficulty retrieving target words. This informal analysis of target-word substitutions should follow the formal assessments discussed above. In particular, it complements interpretation of the accuracy index and should be completed on those individuals whose accuracy scores are lower than the age- or grade-level standard in the presence of a high comprehension percentage (above 90%). Specifically, when analyzing substitutions, the examiner looks for naming patterns that may be unique to the individual under study. Identification of such patterns can provide insights into naming strategies and give direction for remedial goal setting, compensatory programming, and self-advocacy counseling for individuals manifesting word-finding difficulties on the TAWF.

As indicated in Chapter 1 and more extensively in the TAWF *Technical Manual*, various models for analyzing substitution patterns have been discussed in the literature (Coughlan & Warrington, 1978; Fried-Oken, 1984; German, 1982; Helm, 1979). The model developed to analyze the TAWF response patterns incorporates substitution categories drawn from the literature as well as response categories generated from the TAWF standardization sample. Although the categories have been selected on the basis of their appropriateness for the individual naming sections on the TAWF, examiners are encouraged to apply their own knowledge and skills and incorporate additional response classifications when appropriate. The informal nature of this assessment gives the examiner the opportunity to tailor a substitution analysis to a particular person without interfering with the formal assessments of that individual's accuracy and response time on the TAWF. Following are two models for analyzing types of responses produced on the TAWF.

Response Categories for Sections 1, 2, 3, and 5

Individuals' substitution responses to the noun target words on the TAWF can be classified in one of the following categories: semantically related substitutions; perceptually related substitutions; nonspecific words; and other categories such as circumlocutions, self-corrections, and no responses.

Researchers have described many types of semantic or lexical relationships between words (Evens et al., 1983; Lyons, 1977; Riegel, 1970). The following response categories have been adapted from this research to include the most common semantic relationships between TAWF target words and the substitutions given by subjects in responding to the test items in Sections 1, 2, 3, and 5: Superordinate (SUP), Coordinate (CO), Subordinate (SUB), Functional

Attribute (FA), Locative Attribute (LA), Compositional Attribute (COM), Association (A), and Chained (CH). Specifically, the superordinate (SUP) subcategory (sometimes called taxonomy or hyponymy) includes target-word substitutions that name the semantic class in which the target word belongs. The coordinate (CO) subcategory (sometimes called similars or co-hyponyms) represents target-word substitutions from the same semantic class as the target word and from the same level of class inclusion. Most commonly used nouns occur at this coordinate level of class inclusion. Thus, it has been called the "basic object level" (Rosch et al., 1976). The importance of the basic object level in vocabulary development has been documented in the research literature (Anglin, 1977). The subordinate (SUB) subcategory includes responses that represent a subgroup of the target word. Superordinate, coordinate, and subordinate relationships between response substitutions and the target words are considered "logical relations," derived through experience with language and based on abstraction made possible through linguistic categorization and marking (Norlin, 1981). In contrast, "infralogical relations," derived from physical features of the object denoted by the target word (Riegel, 1970), include the next four substitution subcategories. The functional attribute subcategory (FA) represents target-word substitutions that refer to how to use a target word, or they may be responses that represent functional attributes of the target word. Substitutions classified in the locative attribute (LA) subcategory are target-word substitutions that indicate the location of the target word. Responses classified in the compositional attribute (COM) subcategory include target-word substitutions that reflect the material of which the target word is composed. Responses categorized in the association (A) subcategory are those substitutions that represent words that are highly associated with the target word or with a word in the stimulus sentence in Section 2. These are words that often occur with the target word in specific contexts. Chained responses (CH) to noun target words occur when there is a mediated response between the target word and the spoken substitution. The substitution response is linked to the intermediate, rather than the target, word. An example is *shades* for *mask,* where an intermediate *sun glasses* has been omitted in a chain of associated responses. Another example is *pine* for *acorn,* where the omitted intermediate associate is *pine cone.* Chained association response patterns have been described in the concept-development and object-sorting literature by Vygotsky (1986) and Bruner (1973). (See Table 4-1 for descriptions and examples of each of these subcategories.)

The category of perceptual responses consists of subcategories of responses that reflect attention to the auditory attributes of the target word, visual attributes of the target-word referent, or a part of the visual stimulus. Responses showing attention to the lexical or auditory attributes of the target word may be substitutions that are phonemically similar to the target word (PA), responses that include the initial sound or syllable of the target word (IS), responses that are repetitions of words in the test item (R), and target-word substitutions that indicate sounds that may represent the target word (Acoustic Attribute, AA). Responses reflecting attention to visual attributes of the target word may be either visually similar to the target-word referent (VS) or a complete visual misperception of the picture stimulus (VP). An error in the visual misperception subcategory would not be considered a word-finding error, but a misperception. Thus, it would not be included in the error tally. Finally, target-word substitutions indicating the subject under study attended only to a part of the picture or sentence stimulus are classified as part/whole responses (PW). (See Table 4-1 for descriptions and examples of each of these subcategories.)

The nonspecific word category represents substitutions of "general nouns" (Halliday & Hasan, 1976) and includes such subcategories as Indefinite Nouns (IN) ("thing," "something"), General Nouns (GN) (objects, actions, activities), and Unspecified Nouns (UN) ("stuff" or "junk"). Other categories include circumlocutions (C), which are multiword responses that are new phrases or descriptions of the target words. They describe the target word either through its function, its visual attributes, or its location. Excluded from this category are established word combinations in such common use that they may be found in the dictionary. A Substitution plus Self-Correction (SC) is an incorrect response immediately followed by the correct response. The incorrect response may be representative of any one of the classifications presented. This response type indicates that the subject knows the target word but is unable to name it on the first response. Although the subject would receive a score of zero on this item, the item would be scored "yes" in the comprehension assessment to show that he or she knows the target word. When the response to an item is a substitution plus self-correction, the individual's comprehension of the target word does not need to be assessed in Section 6. Finally, the No Response category (NR) marks those items which did not elicit a response within 15 seconds. (Examples and descriptions of these categories are presented in Table 4-1.)

Response Categories for Section 4, Picture Naming: Verbs

Although similar to classifications of responses in naming nouns, response analyses of target-word substitutions in the Picture Naming: Verbs section require consideration of unique substitution categories that are specific to the task of naming verbs. Whereas nominal concepts are organized into hierarchies governed by levels of class inclusion and different kinds of attribution, verbal conceptual hierarchies are shallow or nonexistent (Miller & Johnson-Laird, 1976).

Instead, verbs (especially action verbs) can be thought of as procedures or routines that are related to one another as subroutines. Spatial inclusion, as exemplified by partonomy (versus the class inclusion of taxonomy or hyponymy), has been hypothesized as a useful relation among verbs. Subroutines are

1 Table 4-1
Response Categories for Analyses of Target-Word Substitutions on the TAWF for Sections 1, 2, 3, and 5

Response Category	Code	Description	Example
Semantic			
Superordinate	(SUP)	Target-word substitution that names the semantic class in which the target word belongs.	*alarm* for *siren* *tools* for *silverware* *suit* for *costume* *nut* for *acorn* *horse* for *unicorn* *bone* for *wishbone*
Coordinate	(CO)	Target-word substitution that is at the basic level and/or in the same semantic class as the target word.	*cane* for *crutch* *dominoes* for *dice* *horn* for *harmonica* *spool* for *thimble* *collar* for *leash*
Subordinate	(SUB)	Target-word substitution that represents a subgroup of the target word.	*wire pliers* for *pliers* *Pluto* for *planets*
Functional Attribute	(FA)	Target-word substitution that attends to the use of a target word. May represent functional attributes of the target word.	*helper* for *crutch* *lifter* for *jack* *rower* for *oar* *direction* for *compass*
Locative Attribute	(LA)	Target-word substitution that indicates the location of the target word.	*kitchen* for *appliances* *sentence* for *punctuation* *back* for *saddle* *plant* for *thorn*
Compositional Attribute	(COM)	Target-word substitution that indicates the material of which the target object is composed or conceptual attributes of the target word.	*crust* for *globe* *water* for *rivers* *actions* for *dances* *chain* for *leash* *states* or *cities* for *countries*
Association	(A)	Target-word substitution that represents words that are highly associated with the target word.	*book* for *backpack* *oil* for *funnel* *sweeper* for *dustpan*
Chained	(CH)	Target-word substitution that is linked to an unnamed intermediate word rather than to the target word.	*shades (glasses)* for *mask* *micro (microscope)* for *telescope* *thumb tack (thumb)* for *thimble*

Table 4-1 (continued)
Response Categories for Analyses of Target-Word Substitutions on the TAWF for Sections 1, 2, 3, and 5

Response Category	Code	Description	Example
Perceptual			
Phonemic Attribute	(PA)	Target-word substitution that sounds similar to the target word.	*fishbone* for *wishbone* *tunnel* for *funnel* *dishpan* for *dustpan* *hopcross* for *hopscotch* *pamper* for *hamper* *larva* for *lava*
Initial Sound	(IS)	Target-word substitution that includes the initial sound or syllable of the target word or a discarded response.	*s, s, saddle* *t, t, tattoo* *h, h, palm*
Repetition	(R)	Target-word substitution that is a repetition of words in the test item.	*round model* for *globe* *vegetable garden* for *seed* *fire trucks* for *siren*
Acoustic Attribute	(AA)	Target-word substitution that indicates sounds that may represent the target word.	*boom-boom* for *tambourine* *jingle, jingle* for *tambourine* *humming* for *harmonica*
Visual Substitution	(VS)	Target-word substitution that is visually similar to the target-word referent.	*cubes* for *dice* *box* for *battery* *arrow* for *dart* *horseshoe* for *magnet* *coal* for *lava*
Visual Misperception	(VP)*	Target-word substitution that indicates that the stimulus picture was misperceived.	*fighting* for *dancing* *stamps* for *film*
Part/Whole	(PW)	Target-word substitution that indicates attention to a part of the stimulus.	*plate* for *wishbone* *rim* for *compass* *people* for *ocean*
Nonspecific Words			
Indefinite Noun	(IN)	Target-word substitution that is indefinite.	*things* for *dice*
General Noun	(GN)	Target-word substitution that is overly general.	*objects* for *awards*
Unspecified Nouns	(UN)	Target-word substitution that is nonspecific and provides little information.	*stuff* for *silverware*

*Target-word substitutions indicating that the picture was misperceived are not considered errors.

Table 4-1 (continued) Response Categories for Analyses of Target-Word Substitutions on the TAWF for Sections 1, 2, 3, and 5

Response Category	Code	Description	Example
Other Categories			
Circumlocution	(C)	Multiword response that represents a new phrase for the target word. It may attend to either the semantic or perceptual attributes of the target word. Excluded are established word combinations containing frequently paired words such as *hard hat* for helmet.	*What you believe in* for *religion* *thumb thing* for *thimble* *eating tools* for *silverware*
Substitution plus Self-Correction	(SC)	Target-word substitution in any of the categories above followed by the correct response.	*lakes—no, rivers* *cane—no, crutch* *judge—no, jury* *bowl—no, cone*
No Response	(NR)	No response within the 15-second time period.	no response for *jack*

included in routines by causal or temporal sequencing, as suggested by cognitive scientists investigating scripts (Abbott, Black, & Smith, 1985; Schank & Abelson, 1977). For example, baking may include mixing dough's ingredients, kneading dough, and rolling dough. These verbs are coordinates, on the same level of a hierarchy and semantically close. At the same time, there is a temporal-causal sequence in these actions as procedures or routines (Miller, Galanter, & Pribram, 1960).

Consequently, an individual's substitution responses to the verbal target words on the TAWF can be classified in one of the following general categories: semantically related verbal or noun substitution; perceptually related verbal or noun substitution; and other categories such as Innovative Verb, Circumlocution, Self-Correction, and No Response.

Specifically, the following substitutions representing semantic relationships have been identified: Superordinate Verb (SUPV), Coordinate Verb (COV), Subordinate Verb (SUBV), Pro-Verbal Action (PVA), Related Noun (RN), Associated Verb (AV), and Chained (CH).

Verbal substitutions, semantically related to the target verb, will be either overly general, Pro-Verbal Action (PVA), or fall within the verb target word's hierarchy (taxonomy, hyponymy). As with nouns, within a hierarchy, substitutions can have a superordinate, coordinate, or subordinate relationship to the target word. Superordinate Verb responses (SUPV) are verbal substitutions representing a general action that is superordinate to the target action indicated by the stimulus picture. The Coordinate Verb (COV) subcategory represents verbal target-word substitutions that are closely related to, and seem to be at the same hierarchy level as, the target word. The Subordinate Verb (SUBV) subcategory includes responses that represent a subordinate action or an action in a subgroup of the target word. Pro-Verbal Action responses (PVA) are target verb substitutions that represent overly general verbal pro-forms rather than the specific target verb (Halliday & Hasan, 1976; Lyons, 1977). The Related Noun category (RN) contains noun substitutions that express a relationship to the target verb which implies an end result (hole for drilling), goal (direction of traffic), location, object, or agent. Associated Verb (AV) refers to verbal substitutions that are at some distance from the target verb but that represent actions highly associated with the target verb. Chained responses (CH) to verb target words occur when there is a mediated response between the target word and the spoken substitution, so that the noun or verbal substitution response is linked to the intermediate, rather than the target, word. An example is *desk* for *filing,* where an intermediate *file cabinet* has been omitted in a chain of associated responses. Another example is *diving* for *parachuting,* where the omitted mediate associate is skydiving. Chained-association response patterns have been described in the concept-development and object-sorting literature by Vygotsky (1986) and Bruner (1973).

Since verbal taxonomies are less easily determined than nominal taxonomies, subjective decisions will be required in some classifications, and double coding may be advisable. The key distinction should be one of semantic closeness, with the Superordinate (SUPV), Coordinate (COV), and Subordinate (SUBV) Verb subcategories marking substitutions closest to the target word.

Perceptual responses consist of subcategories that reflect attention to phonemic/lexical or visual attributes of the target word, that are part/whole responses, or that are labels of objects in the picture. Phonemic substitutions and root words are designated as lexical because such substitutions are determined by the acoustic shape of the target word as opposed to the perceptual-stimulus-driven categories of Visual Substitution (VSV), Visual Misperception (VP), Picture Labeling (PL), and Part/Whole responses for verbs (PWV). Those responses reflecting attention to the lexical or phonemic attributes of the target word may be substitutions that are phonemically similar to the target verb (PAV), responses that include the initial sound or syllable of the target verb (ISV), or Root-Word Verbs (RWV)—substitutions that represent the root verb without the "ing" inflectional ending. Failure to produce inflectional endings may be representative of articulation or syntax problems as well as word-finding difficulties; therefore, *substitutions of this nature are not considered word-finding errors and are not scored as incorrect.* Responses reflecting attention to visual attributes of the target word may be either visually similar to the target-word referent (VSV) or a complete visual misperception of the picture stimulus (VP). An error in the visual misperception subcategory would not be considered a word-finding error but a misperception. Thus, it would not be included in the error tally. Part/Whole responses for verbs (PWV) are verbal target-word substitutions that indicate attention to a component act indicated in the picture stimulus *(hanging* for *parachuting).* Nouns labeling parts of the stimulus picture are classified in the Picture Labeling (PL) category and are not acceptable substitutions for the target verb.

Other categories include Innovative Verb (IV), Circumlocution of Verb (CV), Substitution plus Self-Correction (SC), and No Response (NR). Innovative Verb responses (IV), technically called "innovative de-nominal verbs" (Clark, 1982), are verbal responses created when one converts a noun to a verb in an effort to name the target action. Circumlocution of Verb responses (CV) are multiword responses to a target word that represent a new phrase or description of the target word either through its function, its visual attributes, or its location. Excluded from this category are established word combinations that are so commonly used they appear in the dictionary. As with noun targets, a Substitution plus Self-Correction (SC) is an incorrect response immediately followed by the correct response. The incorrect response may be representative of any one of the classifications listed above. This response type indicates that the subject knows the target verb but is unable to name it on the first response. Although the subject would receive no credit when this term is scored, the item would be scored "yes" in the comprehension assessment to indicate that the subject knows the target word. When the response to an item reflects comprehension of the target word with substitution plus self-correction, the individual's comprehension of the target word need not be assessed in Section 6. Finally, the No Response (NR) category refers to those items that did not elicit a response within 15 seconds.

Table 4-2 presents descriptions and examples of each of the response categories identified above for Section 4, Picture Naming: Verbs. Appendix C consists of recommended categories for typical target-word substitutions on the TAWF. Appendix D contains forms that may be used to summarize classifications of TAWF target-word substitutions.

INTERPRETING SECONDARY CHARACTERISTICS

Two types of secondary characteristics may be present when a subject manifests word-finding difficulties: gestures and extra verbalizations. Gestures refer to those nonverbal behaviors that a subject may produce when struggling to find a word. Such gestures may be used to mime the target word, as when a subject points to his wrist to indicate time or to his eyes to indicate the function of binoculars. These gestures may also be behavioral manifestations of frustration at being unable to find the target words, such as facial grimaces, finger snapping, or table tapping. Extra verbalizations refer to any verbal narration that accompanies the subject's efforts to retrieve the target word. These extra verbalizations may be comments about the word-finding process itself such as "I know it, but I can't think of it" or "Wait, don't tell me, I will think of it." This

2 Table 4-2
Response Categories for Analyses of Target-Word Substitutions on the TAWF for Section 4

Response Category	Code	Description	Example
Superordinate Verb	(SUPV)	Verbal target word substitution that represents a general action that is superordinate to the target action.	*storing* for *filing* *walking* for *marching* *policing* for *directing* *photographing* for *developing*
Coordinate Verb	(COV)	Verbal target-word substitution at the basic level that is in the same semantic class as the target word.	*kneading* for *rolling* *screwing* for *drilling* *knotting* for *braiding* *blinking* for *winking*
Subordinate Verb	(SUBV)	Verbal target-word substitution that represents subordinate actions or actions in a subgroup of the target word.	*yanking* for *pulling* *weighing* for *measuring* *stopping* for *directing*
Pro-Verbal Action	(PVA)	Verbal target-word substitution that represents nonspecific, overly general verbals.	*putting* for *plugging* *working* for *grating* *making* for *knitting*
Related Noun	(RN)	Noun target-word substitution that expresses a relationship to the target word such as result, goal, location, object, or agent.	*holes* for *drilling* *hand out* for *begging*
Associated Verb	(AV)	Verbal target-word substitution that may be highly associated with the target word.	*writing* for *measuring* *threading* for *knitting* *flying* for *parachuting* *filming* for *developing*
Chained	(CH)	Target-word substitution that is associated to an unnamed intermediate word rather than to the target word.	*diving (sky diving)* for *parachuting* *desk (file cabinet)* for *filing* *screaming (scraping)* for *grating*
Phonemic Attribute of Verb	(PAV)	Verbal target-word substitution that is auditorily similar to the target word.	*delapping* for *developing* *dipping* for *dripping* *grilling* for *drilling*
Initial Sound of Verb	(ISV)	Target-word substitution that includes the initial sound or syllable of the target word.	*br, br, braiding* for *braiding* *f, f, filing* for *filing* *w, w, weighing* for *weighing*
Root-Word Verb	(RWV)*	Verbal target-word substitution that represents the root verb without the inflectional ending.	*dance* for *dancing* *grate* for *grating* *develop* for *developing*

*Considered an acceptable response.

Table 4-2 (continued)
Response Categories for Analyses of Target-Word Substitutions on the TAWF for Section 4

Response Category	Code	Description	Example
Visual Substitution	(VSV)	Verbal target word substitution that is visually similar to the target word.	*scrubbing* for *grating*
Visual Misperception	(VP)*	Target-word substitution that indicates that the stimulus picture was misperceived.	*giving* for *begging* *offering* for *begging*
Part/Whole	(PWV)	Verbal target-word substitution that indicates attention to a component act indicated in the picture stimulus.	*hanging* for *parachuting* *waving* for *directing* *dipping* for *developing*
Picture Labeling	(PL)	Noun target-word substitution representing an object or person in the picture.	*beggar* for *begging* *needle* for *threading* *police officer* for *directing*
Innovative Verb	(IV)	Verbal target-word substitution that the subject creates by converting a noun to a verb.	*screwdriving* for *drilling* *heighting* for *measuring* *scaling* for *weighing*
Circumlocution of Verb	(CV)	Multiword response that represents a new phrase for the target word. It may attend to either the semantic or perceptual attributes of the target word and may include pro-verbal action responses or associated verb responses. Excluded are established word combinations in common use such as *skydiving* for *parachuting* or *putting in* for *plugging*.	*flying in the air* for *parachuting* *direction of traffic* for *directing* *man on a horse* for *statue*
Substitution plus Self-Correction	(SC)	Target-word substitution in any of the categories above, followed by the correct response.	*screwing—no, drilling* *drop—no, dripping* *taste—no, licking* *playing—no, dancing*
No Response	(NR)	No response within the 15-second time period.	no response for *directing*

*Considered an acceptable response.

behavior may also represent starter phrases that help frame the response such as "it is a ______" or time fillers such as "oh, it's a, um, a______."

Informal analysis of secondary characteristics in a subject's performance on word-finding tasks is completed through observation. The TAWF provides a special procedure for such observations. It is recommended that the examiner indicate with a check (√) next to the target word when a subject manifests these types of struggle behavior. A frequency count is then completed on the number of occurrences of both these behaviors during the naming tasks on the TAWF. Because these verbal and nonverbal secondary characteristics of word-finding problems are often present when a person is having difficulty finding a word, they may signal that the person knows the word under consideration but is having difficulty retrieving it in the given context.

Alone, these informal analyses are not meaningful, but when integrated with the accuracy, time, and comprehension analyses discussed above, they can aid in interpreting a subject's word-finding performance on the TAWF and possibly assist a clinician in planning intervention. For example, the presence of secondary characteristics on 25% or more of the items with a low accuracy score or slow item response time (estimated or actual) and a comprehension score within the 90 to 100% range should further indicate to the examiner that the individual under study may be manifesting word-finding problems on the TAWF (see Appendix A, Figure 1).

IDENTIFICATION OF INDIVIDUALS WITH WORD-FINDING PROBLEMS ON THE TAWF

As indicated above, three types of individuals manifest problems in finding words: those with (a) naming difficulties due to expressive language word-finding problems occurring in the presence of good understanding of language (Type 1), (b) naming difficulties due to underlying problems in understanding language (Type 2), and (c) naming difficulties due both to underlying problems in language comprehension and expressive word-finding deficits (Type 3). The classical definition of word-finding disorders in children refers to Type 1, individuals who have difficulty retrieving words that they understand.

The four profiles of word-finding skills that can be identified on the TAWF are most appropriate for describing Type 1 problems. These profiles are descriptive in nature and do not indicate or imply underlying etiologies for word-finding problems.

PROFILE A: FAST AND INACCURATE NAMER
High Comprehension Scores on the TAWF

Formal Accuracy and Time Evaluations:

a. An inaccurate namer has a standard score that is below 85 (or below the borderline cutoff scores, e.g., 80 or 90), in the presence of a comprehension score of at least 90%.
b. A fast namer has an Estimated Item Response Time or an Average Item Response Time index that is less than the grade- or age-level standard.

Informal Secondary Characteristics Evaluation:

c. The individual may demonstrate a high incidence of gestures or extra verbalizations accompanying attempts to name the target words on the naming tasks.

PROFILE B: SLOW AND INACCURATE NAMER
High Comprehension Scores on the TAWF

Formal Accuracy and Time Evaluations:

a. An inaccurate namer has a standard score that is below 85 (or below the borderline cutoff scores, e.g., 80 or 90), in the presence of a comprehension score of at least 90%.
b. A slow namer has an Estimated Item Response Time or an Average Item Response Time index that is equal to or greater than the grade- or age-level standard.

Informal Secondary Characteristics Evaluation:

c. The individual may manifest a high incidence of gestures or extra verbalizations accompanying attempts to name the target words on the naming tasks.

PROFILE C: FAST AND ACCURATE NAMER
No Word-Finding Problems on the TAWF

Formal Accuracy and Time Evaluations:

a. An accurate namer has a standard score that is above 85 (or above the borderline cutoff score, e.g., 80 or 90), in the presence of a comprehension score of at least 90%.
b. A fast namer has an Estimated Item Response Time or an Average Item Response Time index that is less than the grade- or age-level standard.

Informal Secondary Characteristics Evaluation:

c. The individual does not manifest a high incidence of gestures or extra verbalizations accompanying attempts to name the target words on the naming tasks.

PROFILE D: SLOW AND ACCURATE NAMER
High Comprehension Score on the TAWF

Formal Accuracy and Time Evaluations:

a. An accurate namer has a standard score that is above 85 (or above the borderline cutoff score, e.g., 80 or 90), in the presence of a comprehension score of at least 90%.
b. A slow namer has an Estimated Item Response Time or an Average Item Response Time index that is equal to or greater than the grade- or age-level standard.

Informal Secondary Characteristics Evaluation:

c. The individual may show a high incidence of gestures or extra verbalizations accompanying attempts to name the target words on the naming tasks.

TAWF performances of individuals who are Types 2 and 3 may appear to match these time and accuracy profiles, but because of their low comprehension scores on the target words, these subjects may or may not be classified as manifesting word-finding problems on the TAWF. The performance patterns of the subjects are described below. Such performance patterns may suggest other underlying linguistic disorders.

SLOW AND INACCURATE—LOW COMPREHENSION SCORE ON THE TAWF

Formal Accuracy and Time Evaluations/Type 2 (underlying problem in understanding language):

a. An inaccurate namer has a standard score that is below 85 (or below the borderline cutoff score, e.g., 80 or 90), with a comprehension score less than 90%.
b. A slow namer has an Estimated Item Response Time or an Average Item Response Time index that is equal to or greater than the grade- or age-level standard.

Prorated Accuracy Rescoring Procedure/Type 2:

c. After the response booklet is rescored, the prorated standard score is above 85 (or the 80–90 borderline range). This indicates that the naming errors are only on words that the individual does not know. This suggests some underlying problems with understanding language causing difficulty in finding words, but not a true expressive language word-finding deficit. That is, on words this individual knows, he or she does not have an expressive language word-finding deficit.

Informal Secondary Characteristics Evaluation/Type 2:

d. The individual does not manifest a high incidence of gestures or extra verbalizations accompanying attempts to name the target words on the naming tasks.

Formal Accuracy and Time Evaluations/Type 3 (underlying problem in language comprehension and expressive word-finding deficits):

a. An inaccurate namer has a standard score that is below 85 (or below the borderline cutoff score, e.g., 80 or 90), with a comprehension score less than 90%.
b. A slow namer has an Estimated Item Response Time or an Average Item Response Time index that is equal to or greater than the grade- or age-level standard.

Prorated Accuracy Rescoring Procedure/Type 3:

c. After the response booklet is rescored, the prorated standard score is still below 85 (or below the 80–90 borderline range). This individual has word-finding problems on words that he or she knows and may also have some underlying problems with understanding language, as suggested by the low comprehension scores.

Informal Secondary Characteristics Evaluation/Type 3:

d. On the target words that the individual knows but cannot name, he or she does demonstrate a high incidence of gestures or extra verbalizations when attempting to name the target words on the naming tasks.

FAST AND INACCURATE—LOW COMPREHENSION SCORE ON THE TAWF

Formal Accuracy and Time Evaluations/Type 2 (underlying problem in understanding language):

a. An inaccurate namer has a standard score that is below 85 (or below the borderline cutoff score, e.g., 80 or 90), with a comprehension score less than 90%.
b. A fast namer has an Estimated Item Response Time or an Average Item Response Time index that is less than the grade- or age-level standard.

Prorated Accuracy Rescoring Procedure/Type 2:

c. After the response booklet is rescored, the prorated standard score is above 85 (or above the 80–90 borderline range). The naming errors are only on words that he or she does not know, suggesting an underlying problem in understanding language causing difficulty in finding words, but not a true expressive language word-finding deficit. That is, on words this individual knows, he or she does not have an expressive language word-finding deficit.

Informal Secondary Characteristics Evaluation/Type 2:

d. The individual does not demonstrate a high incidence of gestures or extra verbalizations accompanying attempts to name the target words on the naming tasks.

Formal Accuracy and Time Evaluations/Type 3 (underlying problem in language comprehension and expressive word-finding deficits):

a. An inaccurate namer has a standard score that is below 85 (or below the borderline cutoff score, e.g., 80 or 90), with a comprehension score less than 90%.
b. A fast namer has an Estimated Item Response Time or an Average Item Response Time index that is less than the grade- or age-level standard.

Prorated Accuracy Rescoring Procedure/Type 3:

c. After the response booklet is rescored, the prorated standard score is still below 85 (or the 80–90 borderline range). This individual has word-finding problems on words that he or she knows and may also have some problems understanding language, as suggested by the low comprehension scores.

Informal Secondary Characteristics Evaluation/Type 3:

d. On the target words that the individual knows but cannot name, he or she does demonstrate a high incidence of gestures or extra verbalizations when attempting to name the target words on the naming tasks.

INTERPRETATION CONSIDERATIONS

The TAWF is a carefully developed, thoroughly standardized, and extensively researched instrument designed to provide the examiner with an opportunity to systematically observe an individual's word-finding skills in a set of psychometrically sound naming tasks. Through careful and correct test administration the examiner can gain significant insights into an individual's word-finding skills on the naming tasks employed in the TAWF. However, like all individually administered tests confined to short periods of testing time, use of the TAWF has certain limitations.

The TAWF does not measure all the skills necessary for a complete analysis of word-finding skills. Such an assessment is a multifaceted process that requires numerous observations of an individual's naming of different types of vocabulary in various stimulus contexts across different situational contexts. Although the TAWF provides the examiner with many of these observations (single-word naming in three different stimulus contexts using nouns, verbs, and category words) in standardized conditions, additional assessment may be necessary to determine that an individual has an expressive language problem in word finding. The examiner should use the TAWF to formulate hypotheses about an individual's word-finding skills relative to accuracy and speed and then employ informal follow-up assessment procedures to validate these hypotheses. To verify observations gained from the TAWF, such procedures should include classroom observations of a student under study engaged in expressive language activities, observations of an adult in normal daily activities, and interviews with the student's teachers and parents or the adult's family, friends, and associates. In addition, use of language samples in order to observe an individual's naming skills in connected speech would complement observations made in constrained naming on the TAWF. For example, the examiner could evaluate the individual's spontaneous language for the presence of word-finding behaviors that suggest difficulties in word finding in discourse (German, 1987).

Ultimately, the diagnosis of word-finding problems lies with the clinical judgment of the professional involved. The strength of the TAWF is that it provides opportunities for systematic observations of an individual's word-finding skills in constrained naming and provides the examiner with standardized scores useful in documenting expressive language disorders. However, TAWF findings must be integrated with results from other informal and formal observations and assessments and interpreted by trained professionals before word-finding problems can be determined.

In addition, low TAWF scores do not always mean that an individual has word-finding problems. Other factors may contribute to a poor score. Therefore, caution should be exercised in concluding that an individual who performs poorly on the TAWF is "anomic," "dysnomic," "aphasic," or "language disordered." For example, an assessment of word-finding skills cannot be made unless the examiner is reasonably sure the subject understands the vocabulary utilized in the evaluation. Thus, if a subject receives a low score on the comprehension evaluation on the TAWF, the accuracy score should not be interpreted as signaling a problem in word finding only. In cases of low comprehension, the examiner should follow up with receptive language testing to interpret the low TAWF score as well as evaluate the individual's ability to retrieve words he or she knows (Prorated Accuracy Rescoring procedure). Other factors may affect TAWF results, including motivation, emotional stability, and impulsiveness, as well as cultural, regional, and linguistic differences. When involvement of these factors is suspected, the examiner must investigate the individual's expressive language across situations to clarify low TAWF scores.

Lastly, inferences from the TAWF should not be made with respect to etiology. The TAWF scores do not indicate *why* an individual performs poorly. They only yield an indication of *how* an individual performs in comparison to peers on the content measured. Similarly, the suggested naming profiles are only descriptive in nature; thus, they do not indicate the source of any word-finding difficulties observed on the TAWF. It would be highly inappropriate, therefore, to interpret an individual's behavior on the TAWF as an indication of any underlying neurological pathology. Although many of the theoretical constructs that underlie the TAWF are drawn from studies of adults with neurological problems, the TAWF is not a neurological test. Therefore, even though neurologically disordered adults may manifest problems in word finding, one cannot assume that individuals with word-finding difficulties on the TAWF have neurological disorders. However, findings on the TAWF, when coupled with neurological assessments, can provide examiners with the important information needed to clarify the etiology of word-finding deficits observed on the TAWF.

In summary, the TAWF provides a systematic, controlled set of standardized procedures and conditions for observing word-finding skills in constrained naming tasks. Assessment using the TAWF is not the last, but rather the first, step in a comprehensive evaluation of word-finding skills. The TAWF aids the examiner in forming hypotheses about an individual's expressive language that can be examined in later follow-up procedures. Use of the TAWF to direct and complement follow-up analyses in word finding will provide the examiner with helpful guidance in the overall assessment of an individual's word-finding skills.

CHAPTER FIVE

TAWF BRIEF TEST

INTRODUCTION

Although it is recommended that the entire TAWF be administered for the most reliable and valid assessment of an individual's word-finding skills, there may be occasions where a complete administration is impossible or impractical. In these cases the TAWF Brief Test should be administered. This shortened version of the TAWF may be particularly appropriate for those individuals who are unable to complete the entire TAWF due to test fatigue resulting from their particular disability. This group may include individuals suffering from severe aphasia, Alzheimer's disease, severe attention disorders, or other head traumas that would interfere with test-taking endurance. There may also be testing situations where time constraints make it impractical to administer the complete TAWF (e.g., school or clinic settings where the examiner's or subject's testing time is limited). The TAWF Brief Test may be administered in these situations also. The examiner should remember, however, that although the TAWF Brief Test will give a reasonably reliable assessment of an individual's word-finding skills, the most reliable assessment is achieved when the entire TAWF is administered. In fact, if after choosing to administer the TAWF Brief Test, an examiner wants to continue with the entire TAWF, he or she can use the responses to the items in the TAWF Brief Test without having to administer the items again as part of the total TAWF administration.

The TAWF Brief Test consists of a selection of items from each of the TAWF naming sections. These items are presented together in a separate section in the TAWF *Test Book*. Examiners administering the TAWF Brief Test should turn to that section. Items were selected to make the range of item difficulty in the shortened version as similar as possible to the range of difficulty in the complete TAWF. The following section presents the administration procedures, technical properties, and norm tables for the TAWF Brief Test. The TAWF informal assessment procedures (substitution types, gestures, and extra verbalizations) are referred to in each test section and at the end of this chapter. Completing these informal evaluations in the TAWF Brief Test is optional. The decision to implement these procedures can be based on the subject under study or the nature of the testing situation.

ADMINISTRATION PROCEDURES

SECTION 1, PICTURE NAMING: NOUNS

This section was designed to assess an individual's speed and accuracy when naming pictorial referents of noun target words. The shortened version of this section consists of 2 example pictures, 4 starter pictures, and 14 test pictures representing one- to four-syllable target words of different semantic categories.

The pictures are black-and-white drawings with the target word highlighted in color. The individual is asked to label the colored area of the picture presented. If the entire picture is colored, the individual is asked to name the whole picture.

Following are the starter items and target words for Section 1 of the TAWF Brief Test, listed in the order in which they should be presented. (See Figure 2-2 in Chapter 2 for sample test items from Section 1.)

Examples	Starter Items	Test Items	
A. leaves	A. nose	1. ruler	21. backpack
B. tree	B. thumb	4. statue	26. jack
	C. kite	7. calculator	28. compass
	D. whistle	10. dice	30. pliers
		13. eyebrow	31. dustpan
		15. dart	34. thermos
		19. starfish	37. seahorse

Directions

Although the TAWF Brief Test requires the examiner to administer fewer items in Section 1, the directions for administration are the same for both the shortened form and the complete test. Because these directions are clearly presented in the TAWF *Test Book* and are repeated in Chapter 2 of this manual, they are not repeated again here. The examiner is directed to these other sources for test directions for Section 1, Picture Naming: Nouns.

Marking Responses

Accuracy. With the response booklet open to Section 1, Picture Naming: Nouns, mark a "1" for all correct responses adjacent the test item. For all incorrect responses, record the subject's complete response in the space provided and record a "0" adjacent the test item for which there was an error.

Response Time. The Actual Item Response Time measurement cannot be used with the Brief Test. However, use of a tape recorder during the shortened form would allow the examiner to use the Average Item Response Time norms if the remaining items are administered after the results of the Brief Test have been analyzed. The Actual Item Response Time measurement is described in detail in Chapter 3 of this manual.

The Estimated Item Response Time procedure is optional when using the TAWF Brief Test. When employed, it is used to judge the amount of time it takes a subject to name a target word in Section 1, Picture Naming: Nouns. It is determined by judging whether the time period between the presentation of each stimulus picture and the subject's first effort to name the target word is longer or shorter than 4 seconds. If the examiner chooses to employ the Estimated Item Response Time procedure, he or she should judge the subject's response speed during the administration of the TAWF Brief Test. While the subject names the target word, the examiner judges whether the time between the verbalization of the word NOW and the subject's response is longer or shorter than 4 seconds. The examiner then checks the column adjacent the target item that represents whether the subject's estimated item response time is longer or shorter than the 4-second cutoff. Appendix F gives grade- and age-level standards for the ERT on the Brief Test.

Gestures and Extra Verbalizations. Record gestures and extra verbalizations using the same procedures described for the complete TAWF in Chapter 2 of this manual.

All other spaces and columns in the response booklet are to be completed after the test administration. In summary, during administration of Section 1, record responses in five of the areas on page 2 of the response booklet: *1 or 0, Subject's Response, Estimated Item Response Time procedure, Gesture,* and *Extra Verbal.* (See Figure 2-3 in Chapter 2 for a sample of response recording for Section 1, Picture Naming: Nouns.)

SECTION 2, SENTENCE COMPLETION NAMING

This section was designed to assess a subject's accuracy when naming target words in an intrasensory, auditory, cloze-procedure format. The TAWF Brief Test consists of 2 examples, 4 starter items, and 6 test items (open-ended sentences). All are declarative, present tense sentences with a minimum of two and a maximum of five associations to the target word. The subject is asked to complete the sentence stated by the examiner by naming the target word that would best complete the sentence. Following are the examples, starter items, and test items for Section 2 of the Brief Test. Test items are listed below in the order in which they should be presented. (See Figure 2-4 in Chapter 2 for sample test items from Section 2.)

Examples

Example A: To unlock a door, you need to use a ________ (key).
Example B: At night you sleep in a ________ (bed).

Starter Items

Starter Item A: A bird lays eggs in a ________ (nest).
Starter Item B: An instructor of a football team is the football ________ (coach).
Starter Item C: The outer part of an apple pie is the pie • ________ (crust).
Starter Item D: The net-like structure that a spider weaves is a spider ________ (web).

Test Items

1. When you ride a horse, you sit on a leather ______ (saddle).
4. A scientist looks at small things through a (microscope).
7. It's fun to shake a friendly dog's front ______ (paw).
10. To grow a vegetable in a garden, you plant a ______ (seed).
13. A person who rides racehorses is called a ______ (jockey).
16. The space between rows of seats is the ______ (aisle).

Directions

Although the TAWF Brief Test requires the examiner to administer fewer items in Section 2, the directions for administration are the same for both the short form and the complete test. Because these directions are clearly presented in the TAWF *Test Book* and are repeated in Chapter 2 of this manual, they are not repeated again here. The examiner is directed to these other sources for test directions for Section 2, Sentence Completion Naming.

Marking Responses

Accuracy. With the response booklet open to Section 2, Sentence Completion Naming, mark a "1" for all correct responses adjacent the test item. For all incorrect responses, record the subject's complete response in the space provided and record a "0" adjacent the test item in which there was an error.

Gestures and Extra Verbalizations. Record gestures and extra verbalizations using the same procedures described for the complete TAWF in Chapter 2 of this manual.

All other spaces and columns in the response booklet are to be completed after the test administration. In summary, during administration of Section 2, record responses in four of the columns on page 3 of the response booklet: *1 or 0, Subject's Response, Gesture,* and *Extra Verbal.*

SECTION 3, DESCRIPTION NAMING

This section was designed to assess an individual's accuracy when naming words in an intrasensory auditory task where the individual is required to name a target word implied by a description given by the examiner. Each description includes either or both the semantic category of the target word and a functional attribute and one to three of the following attributes of the implied target word: composition, location, size, and sound. This section consists of 2 examples, 4 starter items, and 4 test items. (See Figure 2-5 for sample test items from Section 3.)

Examples

Example A: What is used to open a door, is made of metal, and is put into a lock? (key)

Example B: What do you sleep in, has a mattress and a pillow, and is in your room? (bed)

Starter Items

Starter Item A: What is used for a bird's home, is made of small pieces of grass, and is found in a tree? (nest)

Starter Item B: What do you find at the beach, is soft to walk on, and is used to build play castles? (sand)

Starter Item C: What part of your face is used for eating, has teeth and a tongue, and is below your nose? (mouth)

Starter Item D: What do you put on an envelope, is rectangular or square, and has glue on the back? (stamp)

Test Items

2. What is a hat that is made of a hard material and is used to protect the head when playing football? (helmet)
5. What is the name of a group of people chosen in court to hear evidence and give a verdict in a trial? (jury)
8. What is the kind of clothing that is funny or strange and is worn on stage or for a special party? (costume)
11. What is the name of the hair that is cut short and brushed down over the forehead? (bangs)

Directions

Although the TAWF Brief Test requires the examiner to administer fewer items in Section 3, the directions for test administration are the same for both the short form and the complete test. Because these directions are clearly presented in the TAWF *Test Book* and are repeated in Chapter 2 of this manual, they are not repeated again here. The examiner is directed to these other sources for test directions for Section 3, Description Naming.

Marking Responses

Accuracy. With the response booklet open to Section 3, Description Naming, mark a "1" for all correct responses adjacent the test item. For all incorrect responses, record the subject's complete response in the space provided and record a "0" adjacent the test item in which there was an error.

Gestures and Extra Verbalizations. Record gestures and extra verbalizations using the same procedures described for the complete TAWF in Chapter 2 of this manual.

All other spaces and columns in the response booklet are to be completed after the test administration. In summary, during administration of Section 3, record responses in four of the columns on page 3 of the response booklet: *1 or 0, Subject's Response, Gesture,* and *Extra Verbal.*

SECTION 4, PICTURE NAMING: VERBS

This section was designed to assess an individual's accuracy in naming action words. Specifically, the subject is shown pictorial representations of 8 verbs (e.g., licking, winking) and asked to label the action in the picture. The section consists of 2 example pictures, 4 starter pictures, and 8 test pictures made up of two- to three-syllable target words that represent verbs in the present participle form (e.g., dripping). The subject is asked to tell what the person or object in the picture is doing. Following are the examples, starter items, and target words for Section 4 of the Brief Test. Items are listed in the order in which they should be presented. (See Figure 2-6 in Chapter 2 for a sample test item from Section 4.)

Examples	Starter Items	Test Items	
A. blowing	A. knocking	2. licking	12. plugging
B. writing	B. catching	5. dripping	14. weighing
	C. diving	8. measuring	17. threading
	D. packing	10. braiding	20. directing

Directions

Although the TAWF Brief Test requires the examiner to administer fewer items in Section 4, the directions for test administration are the same for both the short form and the complete test. Because these directions are clearly presented in the TAWF *Test Book* and are repeated in Chapter 2 of this manual, they are not repeated again here. The examiner is directed to these other sources for test directions for Section 4, Picture Naming: Verbs.

Marking Responses

Accuracy. With the response booklet open to Section 4, Picture Naming: Verbs, mark a "1" for all correct responses adjacent the test item. For all incorrect responses, record the subject's complete response in the space provided and record a "0" adjacent the test item in which there was an error.

Gestures and Extra Verbalizations. Record gestures and extra verbalizations using the same procedures described for the complete TAWF in Chapter 2 of this manual.

All other spaces and columns in the response booklet are to be completed after the test administration. In summary, during administration of Section 4, record responses in four of the columns on page 5 of the response booklet: *1 or 0, Subject's Response, Gesture,* and *Extra Verbal.*

SECTION 5, CATEGORY NAMING

This section was designed to assess an individual's accuracy in naming category words. The section consists of 2 examples, 4 starter items, and 8 test items, each including three subordinate or basic-level words (north, south, east) that imply a target word that names a category (directions). The subject is asked to name the category word for the three subordinate or basic-level words read by the examiner. The examples, starter items, and test items are listed below in the order in which they should be presented. (See Figure 2-7 in Chapter 2 for a sample test item from Section 5.)

Examples	Starter Items	Test Items	
A. numbers	A. birds	1. holidays	13. countries
B. money	B. candy	3. time	16. transportation
	C. days	7. planets	18. appliances
	D. music	10. seasons	19. awards

Directions

Although the TAWF Brief Test requires the examiner to administer fewer items in Section 5, the directions for test administration are the same for both the short form and the complete test. Because these directions are clearly presented in the TAWF *Test Book* and are repeated in Chapter 2 of this manual, they are not repeated again here. The examiner is directed to these other sources for test directions for Section 5, Category Naming.

Marking Responses

Accuracy. With the response booklet open to Section 5, Category Naming, mark a "1" for all correct responses adjacent the test item. For all incorrect responses, record the subject's complete response in the space provided and record a "0" adjacent the test item in which there was an error.

Gestures and Extra Verbalizations. Record gestures and extra verbalizations using the same procedures described for the complete TAWF in Chapter 2 of this manual.

All other spaces and columns in the response booklet are to be completed after the test administration. In summary, during administration of Section 5, record responses in four of the columns on page 6 of the response booklet: *1 or 0, Subject's Response, Gesture,* and *Extra Verbal.*

SECTION 6, COMPREHENSION ASSESSMENT

The purpose of this section is to assess the subject's comprehension of those target words he or she had difficulty naming in the TAWF Brief Test. Although subjects may manifest word-finding difficulties due to underlying comprehension problems, subjects with expressive word-finding disorders have difficulty finding words in the presence of good comprehension of those target words. Therefore, because it is important to determine if target-word comprehension is present before deciding that a response error is an expressive word-finding error, target-word comprehension of all errors must be assessed. This assessment is performed after the TAWF Brief Test is administered. It consists of assessing comprehension only on the items that were named incorrectly during the TAWF Brief Test. Comprehension need not be assessed on items not administered as part of the TAWF Brief Test.

The vocabulary for this comprehension evaluation consists of all the target words in the TAWF Brief Test. Each target word is presented with three decoys in a four-picture format. The comprehension tasks for a specific subject consist of only pictures and sentences representing those target words on which the subject made naming errors. The examiner should turn back in the response booklet to Section 1. For each Brief Test item on which there was a naming error, the examiner should present the corresponding pictures in the test book (see Figure 2-8, Chapter 2). This process is repeated for Sections 2 through 5. Remember, assessment of comprehension does not require naming but uses a recognition response only. The examiner should check target-word comprehension on only those items named incorrectly during the TAWF Brief Test.

Comprehension Assessment for Section 1, Picture Naming: Nouns

In this evaluation the focus is on assessing the subject's knowledge of the target words missed during the Brief Test assessment in Section 1, Picture Naming: Nouns. Present the picture strip for each item in Section 1 to be evaluated, and state the phrase *Point to*____________ with the target word. The subject is to point to the appropriate picture in the strip of four pictures. Proceed in this manner until target-word comprehension of all errors in Section 1 of the Brief Test has been assessed.

Marking Responses

A subject's failure to identify the appropriate picture may be an indication of poor comprehension of that target word and should be checked "no," failure to comprehend the stimulus. The "no" score should be recorded across from the target word in the comprehension column on page 2 of the response booklet. This check indicates that, during the word-finding assessment, the subject may have made a naming error due to lack of knowledge rather than an expressive word-finding problem. If the subject passed the item (a check in the "yes" column), target-word comprehension would be judged adequate for a word-finding assessment and the error in the analysis would be considered a word-finding error. Therefore, the item would be checked "yes" across from the target word in the comprehension column in the response booklet.

Comprehension Assessment for Section 2, Sentence Completion Naming

For errors in Section 2, comprehension of both the sentence and the target word must be verified before a judgment of word-finding skills on a particular item can be made. Begin by presenting the picture strips corresponding to target words missed in Section 2 during the Brief Test. Comprehension of all sentence items missed should be assessed first (Phase 1), followed by an assessment of the subject's knowledge of the target words missed (Phase 2).

Comprehension Assessment of Sentence Items (Phase 1)

Read the following instructions to assess comprehension of the open-ended sentences:

I am going to read some sentences that will have the last word missing. Look at the pictures and point to the one that completes the sentence correctly.

Then read the open-ended sentence missed by the subject and instruct the subject to point to the picture of the word that best completes the sentence. Check the subject's comprehension of all sentence items missed during the Brief Test.

Comprehension Assessment of Target Words (Phase 2)

After assessing comprehension of all sentence items on which there was a naming error, return to the first Brief Test item missed in Section 2 and check comprehension of the target words missed. Read the following:

This time I will tell you to point to a picture that I name. Look carefully at all the pictures and point to the correct picture.

Using the carrier phrase *Point to* ____________ and the target word, ask the subject to identify the picture representing the given word. Check comprehension of all target words missed.

Marking Responses

In the comprehension evaluation, the examiner is interested in knowing if the subject understands both the sentence and the target words missed in the naming section. Failure to identify the picture representing the sentence or the target word may be an indication of poor comprehension of the test item. Failure to comprehend the stimulus should be scored "no." On page 3 of the response booklet, mark a separate check (√) in the "no" columns for the subject's comprehension of the word and for the sentence used to prompt for the target word. However, if the subject passes the sentence and the target-word comprehension evaluation, check "yes" in the comprehension summary column for that item.

Comprehension Assessment for Section 3, Description Naming

For errors in Section 3 (like those in Section 2), comprehension of both the sentence and the target word must be verified before a judgment of word-finding skills on a particular item can be made. Begin by presenting the picture strips corresponding to target words missed in Section 3 during the Brief Test. Comprehension of all sentence items missed should be checked first (Phase 1), followed by an assessment of the subject's knowledge of the target words missed (Phase 2).

Comprehension Assessment of Description Items (Phase 1)

Read the following instructions to assess comprehension of the descriptions:

I am going to read a description of something to you. Look at the pictures and point to the picture that has been described.

Then read the description missed by the subject during the Brief Test and instruct the subject to point to the picture of the word that best fits the description. Check comprehension of all sentence descriptions on which the subject erred.

Comprehension Assessment of Target Words (Phase 2)

After assessing comprehension of all sentence items on which there was a naming error, return to the first missed item in Section 3 and check comprehension of the target words missed. Read the following:

This time I will tell you to point to a picture that I name. Look carefully at all the pictures and point to the correct picture.

Using the carrier phrase *Point to* ___________ and the target word, ask the subject to identify the picture representing the given word. Check comprehension of all target words missed.

Marking Responses

In the comprehension evaluation, the examiner is interested in knowing if the subject understands both the sentence and the target words missed in the naming section. Failure to identify the picture representing the sentence or the target word may be an indication of poor comprehension of the test item. Failure to comprehend the stimulus should be scored "no." On page 4 of the response booklet, mark a separate check (√) in the "no" columns for the subject's comprehension of the word and the sentence used to prompt the target word. However, if the subject passes both the sentence and the target-word comprehension check, mark a check (√) in the "yes" column in the "comprehension summary" column for both the sentence and the target word.

Comprehension Assessment for Section 4, Picture Naming: Verbs

In this evaluation the focus is on assessing the subject's knowledge of the target words missed in the word-finding assessment in Section 4, Picture Naming: Verbs. Present the picture strips corresponding to the items missed in Section 4 during the Brief Test administration and state the phrase *Point to* ____________ with the target word. The subject is to point to the appropriate picture in the strip of four pictures. Proceed in this manner until target-word comprehension of all errors in Section 4 of the Brief Test has been assessed.

Marking Responses

A failure to identify the appropriate pictures may be an indication of poor comprehension of a given target word and should be checked "no," failure to comprehend the stimulus. Check the "no" score across from the target word in the comprehension column on page 5 of the response booklet. This score indicates that during the word-finding assessment the subject may have made a naming error due to lack of knowledge rather than a word-finding problem. If the subject passes the item, target-word comprehension is judged to be adequate for the word-finding assessment, and the error in the analysis is considered a word-finding error. The item is checked "yes" across from the target word in the comprehension column on page 5 of the response booklet.

Comprehension Assessment for Section 5, Category Naming

In this evaluation the focus is on assessing the subject's knowledge of the target words missed in the word-finding assessment in Section 5, Category Naming. Present the pictures representing the items in Section 5 that are to be evaluated, and state the phrase *Point to* ____________ with the target word. The subject is to point to the appropriate picture. Proceed in this manner until target-word comprehension of all errors in Section 5 of the Brief Test has been assessed.

Marking Responses

A subject's failure to identify the appropriate picture may be an indication of poor comprehension of that target word and should be checked "no," failure to comprehend the stimulus. The "no" score should be recorded across from the target word in the comprehension column on page 6 of the response booklet. This check indicates that, during the word-finding assessment, the subject may have made a naming error due to lack of knowledge rather than a word-finding problem. If the subject passed the item (a check in the "yes" column), target-word comprehension would be judged adequate for a word-finding assessment and the error in the analysis would be considered a word-finding error. Therefore, the item would be checked "yes" across from the target word in the comprehension column on page 6 of the response booklet.

SCORING PROCEDURES

ACCURACY SCORING

This section highlights the scoring procedures for each naming section in the TAWF Brief Test. Chapter 3 guides the examiner in the scoring of the entire TAWF. The examiner should review the scoring sections in Chapter 3 for specific scoring details, which also apply to accuracy scoring of the TAWF Brief Test.

Accuracy Raw Scores for Section 1, Picture Naming: Nouns

After administering the TAWF Brief Test items, review the responses recorded in the response booklet for Section 1. Do not score examples or starter items. Opposite the target word indicate with a "1" or "0" whether the subject passed or failed the test item. (See Appendix B for item scoring guidelines.) Always score the subject's first response. Self-corrections of first responses are scored as incorrect.

After scoring the responses, tally the number of correct responses (1's) and enter this total accuracy score in the raw score box labelled "Brief Test Raw Score" at the bottom of page 2 in the response booklet. (See Figure 5-1 for an example of how to calculate the Brief Test Accuracy Raw Score in Section 1 for a sample subject, Art.) Transfer this score to the space provided on the cover of the response booklet.

Accuracy Raw Scores for Section 2, Sentence Completion Naming

After administering the TAWF Brief Test items, review the responses recorded in the response booklet for Section 2. Do not score examples or starter items. Opposite the target word indicate with a "1" or "0" whether the subject passed or failed the test item. (See Appendix B for scoring guidelines.) Always score the individual's first response. Self-corrections of first responses are scored as incorrect. Tally the correct responses and record the total in the "Brief Test Raw Score" box on page 3 of the response booklet. Transfer this score to the space provided on the cover of the response booklet.

Section 1
Picture Naming: Nouns

Starter Items

A. nose	B. thumb	C. kite	D. whistle

Item	1 or 0		Subject's Response	Item Response Time			Ges. (✓)	Ex. Ver. (✓)	Comprehension Yes (✓) No		Response Code (after testing)
				☐ Estimated During Testing		☐ Actual from Tape Recording (sec/hun) (after testing)					
	Brief Test	Complete Test		Less Than 4 sec. (✓)	More Than 4 sec. (✓)				Yes	No	
1. ruler	1					/					
2. mask						/					
3. antenna						/					
4. statue	0		man on a horse			/					
5. crutch						/					
6. suspenders						/					
7. calculator	0		computer			/					
8. palm						/					
9. microphone						/					
10. dice	1					/					
11. chopsticks						/					
12. battery						/					
13. eyebrow	1					/					
14. binoculars						/					
15. dart	1					/					
16. magnet						/					
17. acorn						/					
18. igloo						/					
19. starfish	0		shellfish			/					
20. film						/					
21. backpack	1					/					
22. unicorn						/					
23. harmonica						/					
24. wishbone						/					
25. propeller						/					
26. jack	0		lifter			/					
27. thimble						/					
28. compass						/					
29. funnel						/					
30. pliers	0		wrench			/					
31. dustpan	1					/					
32. hopscotch						/					
33. blimp						/					
34. thermos	0		coffee cup			/					
35. tambourine						/					
36. spatula						/					
37. seahorse	0		dragon fish			/					

Brief Test Raw Score	RAW SCORE	Total Delayed Items	Total Item Response Time	Ges. Total	Ex. Ver. Total	Comprehension Total
6			/			(total unknown)

2

Figure 5-1. Calculating the raw score for accuracy on Section 1 of the TAWF Brief Test (response booklet, page 2).

Accuracy Raw Scores for Section 3, Description Naming

After administering the TAWF Brief Test, review the responses recorded in the response booklet for Section 3. Do not score examples or starter items. Opposite the target word indicate with a "1" or "0" whether the subject passed or failed the test item. (See Appendix B for scoring guidelines.) Always score the individual's first response. Self-corrections of first responses are scored as incorrect. Tally the number of correct responses (1's) and enter the total in the "Brief Test Raw Score" box at the bottom of page 4 in the response booklet. Transfer this score to the space provided on the cover of the response booklet.

Accuracy Raw Scores for Section 4, Picture Naming: Verbs

After administering the TAWF Brief Test, review the responses recorded for Section 4 in the response booklet. Do not score examples or starter items. Opposite the target word indicate with a "1" or "0" whether the subject passed or failed the test item. (See Appendix B for scoring guidelines.) Always score the individual's first response. Self-corrections of first responses are scored as incorrect. Tally the number of correct responses (1's) and enter the total in the "Brief Test Raw Score" box at the bottom of page 5 in the response booklet. Transfer this score to the space provided on the cover of the response booklet.

Accuracy Raw Scores for Section 5, Category Naming

After administering the TAWF Brief Test items, review the responses recorded for Section 5 in the response booklet. Do not score examples or starter items. Opposite the target word indicate with a "1" or "0" whether the subject passed or failed the test item. (See Appendix B for scoring guidelines.) Always score the individual's first response. Self-corrections of first responses are scored as incorrect. Tally the number of correct responses (1's) and enter the total in the "Brief Test Raw Score" box at the bottom of page 6 in the response booklet. Transfer this score to the space provided on the cover of the response booklet.

DETERMINING THE TOTAL RAW SCORE FOR THE TAWF BRIEF TEST

Individual accuracy scores from the five naming sections should be totaled because TAWF Brief Test norms reflect total scores based on all five naming sections. This raw score total is calculated on the cover of the response booklet. Add the number of correct items in each of the five naming sections and enter the total in the space on the response booklet cover labelled "Total Raw Score." (Figure 5-2 presents an example of how to determine the TAWF Brief Test Total Raw Score for a sample subject.)

Accuracy Score Summary

Section	Raw Score Brief Test	Raw Score Complete Test
1. Picture Naming: Nouns	6	
2. Sentence Completion Naming	4	
3. Description Naming	3	
4. Picture Naming: Verbs	6	
5. Category Naming	7	
TOTAL RAW SCORE	26	

Figure 5-2. Calculating TAWF Brief Test Total Raw Score (response booklet, page 1).

CONVERTING THE RAW SCORE TO DERIVED SCORES

The examiner should next convert the raw score to the derived scores. Two types of derived scores, based either on age-group (ages 12 through 80) or grade-group (grades 7 through 12) distributions, are available for the TAWF Brief Test: standard scores and percentile ranks. These norms allow the examiner to compare an individual's TAWF Brief Test scores with the results of subjects of the same chronological age in the standardization sample and, in the case of students, with subjects in the same grade.

Standard errors of measurement for each TAWF Brief Test standard score are also provided. Tables 5-1 through 5-7, located at the end of this chapter, provide standard scores, standard errors of measurement, and percentile ranks for the TAWF Brief Test.

Standard Scores

To determine age-based standard scores, use the subject's age to select the appropriate norm table. Enter the table by locating the subject's Brief Test Total Raw Score in the left column. Reading across from the raw score, locate the corresponding standard score in the standard score column. This represents the individual's standard score for accuracy. Record this score in the appropriate space in the Accuracy Score Summary on the cover of the response booklet (see Figure 5-3). To determine the grade-based standard score for a student, use the same procedure but with the appropriate norm table for the student's

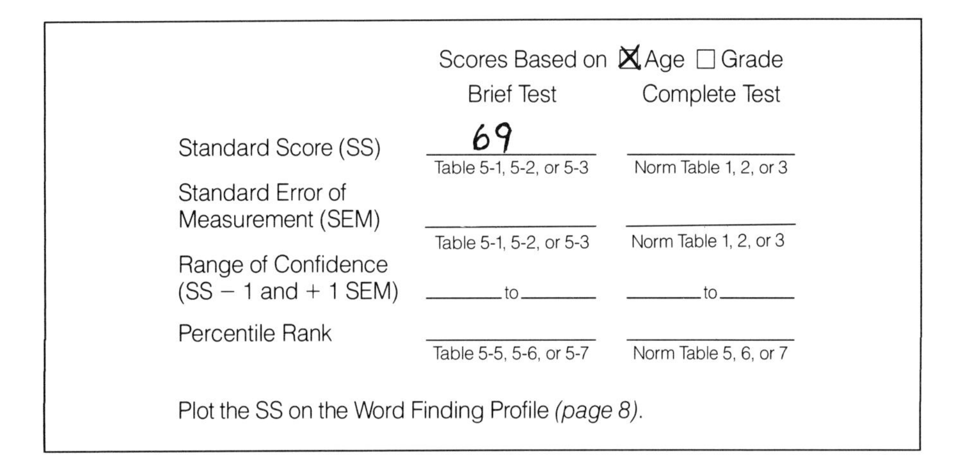

Figure 5-3. Recording age-based standard scores for the TAWF Brief Test (response booklet, page 1).

grade. Note that if a subject receives a raw score lower than the lowest value given in the appropriate table, the standard score assigned is recorded as "less than" the lowest standard score shown.

Standard Error of Measurement and Range of Confidence Scores

Although it is recommended that the entire TAWF be administered, the TAWF Brief Test may be used with some individuals to make significant decisions about their expressive language skills. Therefore, interpretation of an obtained score should consider measurement error. The statistic used to account for measurement error is the Standard Error of Measurement (SEM), further discussed in the TAWF *Technical Manual.* It is recommended that the examiner use the SEM for an individual's obtained score to determine the range of confidence within which the individual's true score is expected to fall. To determine this range of confidence for the individual's standard score, the examiner first needs to identify the SEM for the standard score obtained by the person. SEMs for each standard score on the TAWF Brief Test are presented in Table 5-4. Enter the appropriate table at the individual's standard score and locate the corresponding SEM. Then record the SEM in the appropriate space in the Accuracy Score Summary on the cover of the response booklet.

Next, the examiner should determine the range of confidence for the obtained score. To calculate the upper and lower limits of the range of confidence, subtract the recorded SEM from the standard score and enter this lower limit in the appropriate space on the cover of the booklet; then add the SEM to the standard score and record this upper limit in the appropriate space (see Figure 5-4).

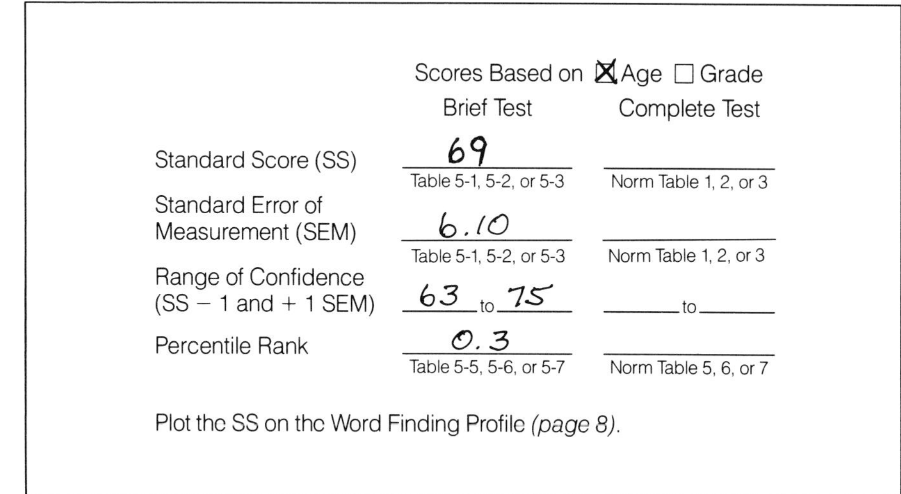

Scores Based on ☒ Age ☐ Grade

	Brief Test	Complete Test
Standard Score (SS)	69 Table 5-1, 5-2, or 5-3	 Norm Table 1, 2, or 3
Standard Error of Measurement (SEM)	6.10 Table 5-1, 5-2, or 5-3	 Norm Table 1, 2, or 3
Range of Confidence (SS − 1 and + 1 SEM)	63 to 75	___ to ___
Percentile Rank	0.3 Table 5-5, 5-6, or 5-7	 Norm Table 5, 6, or 7

Plot the SS on the Word Finding Profile *(page 8)*.

Figure 5-4. Recording the range of confidence for a TAWF Brief Test standard score (response booklet, page 1).

Percentile Rank

To determine age-based percentile ranks, use the subject's age to select the appropriate norm table. Enter the table by locating the individual's Brief Test Total Raw Score in the left column. Reading across from the raw score, locate the corresponding percentile rank in the percentile rank column. This represents the individual's percentile rank for accuracy. The examiner should record the percentile score in the appropriate space in the Accuracy Score Summary for the TAWF Brief Test on the cover of the response booklet. To determine the grade-based percentile rank for a student, use the same procedure but with the appropriate norm table for the student's grade.

RESPONSE-TIME EVALUATION

The purpose of the response-time evaluation is to measure an individual's speed in naming. There is only one procedure that can be used to determine speed of naming on the TAWF Brief Test, the Estimated Item Response Time procedure.

Estimated Item Response Time Procedure

The Estimated Item Response Time (ERT) procedure is used to judge the amount of time it takes an individual to name a target word in Section 1, Picture Naming: Nouns on the TAWF Brief Test. It is determined during administration of the test by judging whether the time period between the presentation of each stimulus picture and the individual's first effort to name the target word is greater than or less than 4 seconds. The examiner simply checks the column adjacent the target item that indicates whether the response delay was greater than or less than the 4-second cut off. See Appendix F for the grade- or age-level standards for the ERT procedure.

Completing the Estimated Item Response Time Procedure

After judging the ERT for each target word in Section 1, tally the number of response delays judged to be 4 seconds or longer (number of checks in the "greater than" column). Enter this number in the appropriate space at the bottom of page 2 in the response booklet. (Figure 5-1 shows how to tally ERT judgments.) Transfer this number to the space provided on the cover of the response booklet. Compare the number of response delays (4 seconds or longer) to the TAWF Brief Test grade- or age-level standard for the subject. Subjects exhibiting a number of response delays (4 seconds or longer) greater than their grade- or age-level standard are considered Slow Namers. Subjects exhibiting a number of response delays (4 seconds or longer) equal to or less than their level standard are considered Fast Namers. Note that in most cases subjects need exhibit only two response delays (4 seconds or longer) to be classified as Slow Namers on the TAWF Brief Test. Therefore, for individuals whose time scores fall in the borderline range, examiners may choose to administer the complete TAWF to clarify naming speed on a longer set of items.

COMPLETING THE COMPREHENSION SUMMARY

After completing the Accuracy Score Summary for the TAWF Brief Test, the examiner should complete the Comprehension Summary. The Comprehension Summary enables the examiner to distinguish between naming errors on words the subject did comprehend and errors on words the subject did not comprehend. The procedures for administering and scoring the Comprehension Summary, explained in Chapter 3 for the full TAWF, are the same for the TAWF Brief Test except that only items in error on the Brief Test should be checked for the Comprehension Summary on the Brief Test. The examiner should then sum the comprehension totals in each section, enter this sum on page 7 of the response booklet, and compute the percentage of comprehension as described in Chapter 3 (except that words known should be divided by 40, the total number of items on the Brief Test, rather than by 107, the total number of items on the full TAWF). Finally, if the subject's percentage of comprehension is below 90%, the examiner should employ the Prorated Accuracy Rescoring procedure described in Chapter 3. This procedure is appropriate for individuals who are suspected of having problems in understanding language but whose expressive word-finding skills are unclear.

GESTURES AND EXTRA VERBALIZATIONS SUMMARY

Gestures and extra verbalizations expressed by the subject when encountering naming difficulty may be noted by the examiner on the response booklet during administration of the TAWF Brief Test. See Chapter 3 for a description of how to record these responses, Chapter 4 for an interpretation of these findings, and Appendix A for a completed response booklet showing such responses.

SUBSTITUTION TYPE SUMMARY

A useful informal evaluation of word-finding problems is the analysis of the types of substitutions manifested by the subject when having difficulty naming target words. This analysis complements the accuracy assessment and may be completed on those subjects whose TAWF Brief Test standard scores are below 85 or are in the 78–92 borderline range in the presence of a comprehension score of 90% or higher (this procedure is optional). For those individuals whose comprehension score is low, analyze the response substitutions of those target words that were misnamed during the Brief Test but known during the comprehension assessment. See Chapter 3 for a description of substitution analysis procedures, Chapter 4 for an explanation and examples of the substitution response categories, and Appendices B and C for descriptions and examples of various substitutions. Appendix D provides forms for the substitution analysis.

USING BOTH: TAWF BRIEF TEST AND COMPLETE TAWF

As indicated above, the TAWF Brief Test will give a reasonably reliable assessment of an individual's word-finding skills, but the most reliable assessment will be achieved when the entire TAWF is administered. Therefore, occasions may arise where an examiner may want to follow up the TAWF Brief Test with a complete administration of the entire TAWF. For example, an individual's word-finding deficits may not be evident on the shortened version of the TAWF, in which case the complete TAWF would need to be administered to draw out the word-finding deficits. In another case, the TAWF Brief Test may clearly indicate an individual's word-finding difficulties, but the examiner may choose to complete the entire TAWF to more extensively observe and contrast the individual's substitution types and secondary characteristics. Thus, after administering the TAWF Brief Test, if an examiner wants to complete the entire TAWF, he or she should do so by administering only the remaining TAWF items. The scores on the Brief Test items can be used in calculating the total TAWF score.

1 Table 5-1
TAWF Brief Test Standard Scores for Adolescents by Age Level

Total Raw Score	Standard Score	Standard Score SEM	Total Raw Score	Standard Score	Standard Score SEM
12–0 to 12–11 yrs			**13–0 to 13–11 yrs**		
<10	<39	6.59	<10	<39	6.59
10	39	6.59	10	39	6.59
11	41	6.43	11	41	6.43
12	44	6.26	12	44	6.26
13	46	6.10	13	46	6.10
14	49	6.10	14	49	6.10
15	51	5.93	15	51	5.93
16	54	5.93	16	54	5.93
17	56	5.93	17	56	5.93
18	58	5.77	18	58	5.77
19	60	5.77	19	60	5.77
20	62	5.77	20	62	5.77
21	65	5.77	21	65	5.77
22	67	5.77	22	67	5.77
23	69	5.93	23	69	5.93
24	71	5.93	24	71	5.93
25	74	5.93	25	74	5.93
26	76	6.10	26	76	6.10
27	79	6.10	27	79	6.10
28	81	6.26	28	81	6.26
29	84	6.43	29	84	6.43
30	86	6.59	30	86	6.59
31	89	6.76	31	89	6.76
32	92	6.92	32	92	6.92
33	96	7.25	33	96	7.25
34	99	7.75	34	99	7.75
35	104	8.24	35	104	8.24
36	108	9.07	36	108	9.07
37	114	10.22	37	114	10.22
38	123	12.20	38	123	12.20
39	136	16.81	39	136	16.81
40	149	21.46	40	149	21.46

Table 5-1 (continued)
TAWF Brief Test Standard Scores for Adolescents by Age Level

Total Raw Score	Standard Score	Standard Score SEM	Total Raw Score	Standard Score	Standard Score SEM
14–0 to 14–11 yrs			**15–10 to 15–11 yrs**		
<10	<36	6.59	<10	<31	6.59
10	36	6.59	10	31	6.59
11	39	6.43	11	34	6.43
12	41	6.26	12	37	6.26
13	44	6.10	13	39	6.10
14	46	6.10	14	41	6.10
15	48	5.93	15	44	5.93
16	51	5.93	16	46	5.93
17	53	5.93	17	48	5.93
18	55	5.77	18	51	5.77
19	57	5.77	19	53	5.77
20	60	5.77	20	55	5.77
21	62	5.77	21	57	5.77
22	64	5.77	22	59	5.77
23	66	5.93	23	62	5.93
24	69	5.93	24	64	5.93
25	71	5.93	25	66	5.93
26	73	6.10	26	69	6.10
27	76	6.10	27	71	6.10
28	78	6.26	28	74	6.26
29	81	6.43	29	76	6.43
30	84	6.59	30	79	6.59
31	86	6.76	31	82	6.76
32	90	6.92	32	85	6.92
33	93	7.25	33	88	7.25
34	97	7.75	34	92	7.75
35	101	8.24	35	96	8.24
36	106	9.07	36	101	9.07
37	112	10.22	37	107	10.22
38	120	12.20	38	115	12.20
39	133	16.81	39	128	16.81
40	146	21.46	40	141	21.46

Table 5-1 (continued)
TAWF Brief Test Standard Scores for Adolescents by Age Level

Total Raw Score	Standard Score	Standard Score SEM	Total Raw Score	Standard Score	Standard Score SEM
16–0 to 16–11 yrs			**17–0 to 19–11 yrs**		
<10	<31	6.59	<10	<29	6.59
10	31	6.59	10	29	6.59
11	34	6.43	11	32	6.43
12	37	6.26	12	34	6.26
13	39	6.10	13	37	6.10
14	41	6.10	14	39	6.10
15	44	5.93	15	42	5.93
16	46	5.93	16	44	5.93
17	48	5.93	17	46	5.93
18	51	5.77	18	48	5.77
19	53	5.77	19	51	5.77
20	55	5.77	20	53	5.77
21	57	5.77	21	55	5.77
22	59	5.77	22	57	5.77
23	62	5.93	23	60	5.93
24	64	5.93	24	62	5.93
25	66	5.93	25	64	5.93
26	69	6.10	26	66	6.10
27	71	6.10	27	69	6.10
28	74	6.26	28	71	6.26
29	76	6.43	29	74	6.43
30	79	6.59	30	77	6.59
31	82	6.76	31	80	6.76
32	85	6.92	32	83	6.92
33	88	7.25	33	86	7.25
34	92	7.75	34	90	7.75
35	96	8.24	35	94	8.24
36	101	9.07	36	99	9.07
37	107	10.22	37	105	10.22
38	115	12.20	38	113	12.20
39	128	16.81	39	126	16.81
40	141	21.46	40	139	21.46

2 Table 5-2
TAWF Brief Test Standard Scores for Adolescents by Grade Level

Total Raw Score	Standard Score	Standard Score SEM	Total Raw Score	Standard Score	Standard Score SEM
Grade 7			**Grade 8**		
<10	<39	6.59	<10	<37	6.59
10	39	6.59	10	37	6.59
11	42	6.43	11	40	6.43
12	44	6.26	12	42	6.26
13	47	6.10	13	45	6.10
14	49	6.10	14	47	6.10
15	52	5.93	15	50	5.93
16	54	5.93	16	52	5.93
17	56	5.93	17	54	5.93
18	59	5.77	18	57	5.77
19	61	5.77	19	59	5.77
20	63	5.77	20	61	5.77
21	65	5.77	21	64	5.77
22	68	5.77	22	66	5.77
23	70	5.93	23	68	5.93
24	72	5.93	24	70	5.93
25	75	5.93	25	73	5.93
26	77	6.10	26	75	6.10
27	80	6.10	27	78	6.10
28	82	6.26	28	80	6.26
29	85	6.43	29	83	6.43
30	88	6.59	30	86	6.59
31	90	6.76	31	89	6.76
32	94	6.92	32	92	6.92
33	97	7.25	33	95	7.25
34	101	7.75	34	99	7.75
35	105	8.24	35	103	8.24
36	110	9.07	36	108	9.07
37	116	10.22	37	114	10.22
38	125	12.20	38	123	12.20
39	138	16.81	39	136	16.81
40	151	21.46	40	149	21.46

Table 5-2 (continued)
TAWF Brief Test Standard Scores for Adolescents by Grade Level

Total Raw Score	Standard Score	Standard Score SEM	Total Raw Score	Standard Score	Standard Score SEM
Grade 9			**Grade 10**		
<10	<31	6.59	<10	<31	6.59
10	31	6.59	10	31	6.59
11	33	6.43	11	33	6.43
12	36	6.26	12	36	6.26
13	39	6.10	13	39	6.10
14	41	6.10	14	41	6.10
15	44	5.93	15	44	5.93
16	46	5.93	16	46	5.93
17	48	5.93	17	48	5.93
18	50	5.77	18	50	5.77
19	53	5.77	19	53	5.77
20	55	5.77	20	55	5.77
21	57	5.77	21	57	5.77
22	60	5.77	22	60	5.77
23	62	5.93	23	62	5.93
24	64	5.93	24	64	5.93
25	67	5.93	25	67	5.93
26	69	6.10	26	69	6.10
27	71	6.10	27	71	6.10
28	74	6.26	28	74	6.26
29	77	6.43	29	77	6.43
30	79	6.59	30	79	6.59
31	82	6.76	31	82	6.76
32	85	6.92	32	85	6.92
33	89	7.25	33	89	7.25
34	93	7.75	34	93	7.75
35	97	8.24	35	97	8.24
36	102	9.07	36	102	9.07
37	108	10.22	37	108	10.22
38	116	12.20	38	116	12.20
39	130	16.81	39	130	16.81
40	143	21.46	40	143	21.46

Table 5-2 (continued)
TAWF Brief Test Standard Scores for Adolescents by Grade Level

Total Raw Score	Standard Score	Standard Score SEM	Total Raw Score	Standard Score	Standard Score SEM
Grade 11			**Grade 12**		
<10	<29	6.59	<10	<26	6.59
10	29	6.59	10	26	6.59
11	32	6.43	11	28	6.43
12	34	6.26	12	31	6.26
13	37	6.10	13	34	6.10
14	39	6.10	14	36	6.10
15	42	5.93	15	38	5.93
16	44	5.93	16	41	5.93
17	46	5.93	17	43	5.93
18	49	5.77	18	45	5.77
19	51	5.77	19	48	5.77
20	53	5.77	20	50	5.77
21	56	5.77	21	52	5.77
22	58	5.77	22	55	5.77
23	60	5.93	23	57	5.93
24	62	5.93	24	59	5.93
25	65	5.93	25	61	5.93
26	67	6.10	26	64	6.10
27	70	6.10	27	66	6.10
28	72	6.26	28	69	6.26
29	75	6.43	29	72	6.43
30	78	6.59	30	74	6.59
31	81	6.76	31	77	6.76
32	84	6.92	32	80	6.92
33	87	7.25	33	84	7.25
34	91	7.75	34	88	7.75
35	95	8.24	35	92	8.24
36	100	9.07	36	97	9.07
37	106	10.22	37	103	10.22
38	115	12.20	38	111	12.20
39	128	16.81	39	125	16.81
40	141	21.46	40	138	21.46

3 Table 5-3
TAWF Brief Test Standard Scores for Adults by Age Level

Total Raw Score	Standard Score	Standard Score SEM	Total Raw Score	Standard Score	Standard Score SEM
20–0 to 39–11 yrs			**40–0 to 59–11 yrs**		
<10	<27	6.59	<10	<32	6.59
10	27	6.59	10	32	6.59
11	30	6.43	11	34	6.43
12	32	6.26	12	37	6.26
13	34	6.10	13	39	6.10
14	36	6.10	14	41	6.10
15	38	5.93	15	43	5.93
16	40	5.93	16	45	5.93
17	42	5.93	17	47	5.93
18	44	5.77	18	49	5.77
19	46	5.77	19	51	5.77
20	48	5.77	20	53	5.77
21	50	5.77	21	55	5.77
22	52	5.77	22	57	5.77
23	54	5.93	23	59	5.93
24	56	5.93	24	61	5.93
25	58	5.93	25	63	5.93
26	60	6.10	26	65	6.10
27	62	6.10	27	67	6.10
28	64	6.26	28	69	6.26
29	67	6.43	29	71	6.43
30	69	6.59	30	74	6.59
31	71	6.76	31	76	6.76
32	74	6.92	32	79	6.92
33	77	7.25	33	82	7.25
34	80	7.75	34	85	7.75
35	84	8.24	35	89	8.24
36	88	9.07	36	93	9.07
37	93	10.22	37	98	10.22
38	100	12.20	38	105	12.20
39	112	16.81	39	117	16.81
40	123	21.46	40	128	21.46

Table 5-3 (continued)
TAWF Brief Test Standard Scores for Adults by Age Level

Total Raw Score	Standard Score	Standard Score SEM
60–0 to 80–0 yrs		
<10	<45	6.59
10	45	6.59
11	47	6.43
12	49	6.26
13	51	6.10
14	53	6.10
15	56	5.93
16	58	5.93
17	60	5.93
18	61	5.77
19	63	5.77
20	65	5.77
21	67	5.77
22	69	5.77
23	71	5.93
24	73	5.93
25	75	5.93
26	77	6.10
27	79	6.10
28	81	6.26
29	84	6.43
30	86	6.59
31	89	6.76
32	91	6.92
33	94	7.25
34	97	7.75
35	101	8.24
36	105	9.07
37	111	10.22
38	118	12.20
39	129	16.81
40	140	21.46

4 Table 5-4
Rasch Standard Errors of Measurement for TAWF-Ability Levels Obtained from the TAWF Brief Test

Raw Scores	TAWF-Ability Level	Standard Error of Measurement
10	−1.33	.40
11	−1.18	.39
12	−1.04	.38
13	−.90	.37
14	−.76	.37
15	−.63	.36
16	−.50	.36
17	−.37	.36
18	−.25	.35
19	−.12	.35
20	.00	.35
21	.12	.35
22	.25	.35
23	.37	.36
24	.50	.36
25	.63	.36
26	.76	.37
27	.90	.37
28	1.04	.38
29	1.18	.39
30	1.33	.40
31	1.50	.41
32	1.67	.42
33	1.86	.44
34	2.06	.47
35	2.30	.50
36	2.57	.55
37	2.91	.62
38	3.36	.74
39	4.10	1.02
40	4.82	1.30

5 Table 5-5
TAWF Brief Test Percentile Ranks for Adolescents by Age Level

Total Raw Score	Percentile Rank	Total Raw Score	Percentile Rank	Total Raw Score	Percentile Rank
12–0 to 12–11 yrs		**13–0 to 13–11 yrs**		**14–0 to 14–11 yrs**	
21	0.1	21	0.1	21	0.1
22	0.4	22	0.1	22	0.1
23	1.0	23	1.0	23	0.1
24	2.0	24	1.0	24	0.4
25	3.0	25	2.0	25	1.0
26	5.0	26	3.0	26	2.0
27	8.0	27	6.0	27	4.0
28	10.0	28	8.0	28	7.0
29	14.0	29	11.0	29	10.0
30	18.0	30	15.0	30	13.0
31	24.0	31	20.0	31	18.0
32	36.0	32	28.0	32	26.0
33	47.0	33	38.0	33	36.0
34	57.0	34	51.0	34	45.0
35	64.0	35	63.0	35	54.0
36	74.0	36	71.0	36	65.0
37	85.0	37	81.0	37	79.0
38	94.0	38	91.0	38	90.0
39	99.0	39	97.0	39	96.0
40	99.5	40	99.0	40	99.0
15–0 to 15–11 yrs		**16–0 to 16–11 yrs**		**17–0 to 19–11 yrs**	
21	0.1	21	0.1	21	0.1
22	0.1	22	0.1	22	0.1
23	0.1	23	0.1	23	0.1
24	0.1	24	0.1	24	0.1
25	0.4	25	0.1	25	0.1
26	1.0	26	0.3	26	0.1
27	2.0	27	1.0	27	0.4
28	3.0	28	2.0	28	1.0
29	4.0	29	3.0	29	2.0
30	8.0	30	6.0	30	5.0
31	12.0	31	11.0	31	7.0
32	19.0	32	16.0	32	12.0
33	27.0	33	21.0	33	17.0
34	35.0	34	28.0	34	25.0
35	46.0	35	40.0	35	37.0
36	59.0	36	54.0	36	51.0
37	71.0	37	69.0	37	67.0
38	86.0	38	83.0	38	81.0
39	96.0	39	93.0	39	92.0
40	99.0	40	99.0	40	97.0

6 Table 5-6
TAWF Brief Test Percentile Ranks for Adolescents by Grade Level

Total Raw Score	Percentile Rank	Total Raw Score	Percentile Rank	Total Raw Score	Percentile Rank
Grade 7		**Grade 8**		**Grade 9**	
21	0.1	21	0.1	21	0.1
22	0.4	22	0.1	22	0.1
23	1.0	23	0.3	23	0.1
24	2.0	24	0.8	24	0.1
25	3.0	25	2.0	25	0.5
26	6.0	26	3.0	26	1.0
27	8.0	27	5.0	27	3.0
28	14.0	28	7.0	28	5.0
29	18.0	29	11.0	29	7.0
30	23.0	30	15.0	30	11.0
31	30.0	31	20.0	31	16.0
32	36.0	32	29.0	32	21.0
33	48.0	33	41.0	33	28.0
34	58.0	34	52.0	34	38.0
35	66.0	35	62.0	35	49.0
36	75.0	36	73.0	36	59.0
37	86.0	37	87.0	37	72.0
38	93.0	38	91.0	38	88.0
39	98.0	39	98.0	39	95.0
40	99.8	40	99.1	40	99.0
Grade 10		**Grade 11**		**Grade 12**	
21	0.1	21	0.1	21	0.1
22	0.1	22	0.1	22	0.1
23	0.1	23	0.1	23	0.1
24	0.1	24	0.1	24	0.1
25	0.1	25	0.1	25	0.1
26	0.2	26	0.1	26	0.1
27	1.0	27	0.5	27	0.3
28	2.0	28	2.0	28	1.0
29	4.0	29	3.0	29	3.0
30	7.0	30	5.0	30	4.0
31	12.0	31	9.0	31	6.0
32	17.0	32	14.0	32	9.0
33	24.0	33	20.0	33	14.0
34	32.0	34	27.0	34	19.0
35	45.0	35	39.0	35	31.0
36	58.0	36	54.0	36	46.0
37	71.0	37	70.0	37	62.0
38	86.0	38	83.0	38	80.0
39	95.0	39	94.0	39	92.0
40	99.0	40	99.0	40	98.0

7 Table 5-7

TAWF Brief Test Percentile Ranks for Adults by Age Level

Total Raw Score	Percentile Rank	Total Raw Score	Percentile Rank	Total Raw Score	Percentile Rank
20–0 to 39–11 yrs		**40–0 to 59–11 yrs**		**60–0 to 80–0 yrs**	
21	0.1	21	0.1	21	0.1
22	0.1	22	0.1	22	0.1
23	0.1	23	0.1	23	0.4
24	0.1	24	0.1	24	1.0
25	0.1	25	0.1	25	2.0
26	0.1	26	0.2	26	4.0
27	0.1	27	0.4	27	5.0
28	0.2	28	1.0	28	8.0
29	0.5	29	2.0	29	12.0
30	1.0	30	3.0	30	18.0
31	2.0	31	4.0	31	25.0
32	4.0	32	7.0	32	31.0
33	6.0	33	11.0	33	38.0
34	9.0	34	16.0	34	47.0
35	15.0	35	24.0	35	58.0
36	24.0	36	35.0	36	69.0
37	38.0	37	48.0	37	77.0
38	56.0	38	65.0	38	86.0
39	73.0	39	84.0	39	95.0
40	91.0	40	96.0	40	99.3

REFERENCES

Abbott, V., Black J., & Smith, E. (1985). The representation of scripts in memory. *Journal of Memory and Language, 24,* 179–199.

Anglin, J. M. (1977). *Word, object, and conceptual development.* New York: W. W. Norton.

Barten, S. S. (1979). Development of gestures. In N. R. Smith & M. B. Franklin (Eds.), *Symbolic functioning in childhood* (pp. 139–151). Hillsdale, NJ: Lawrence Erlbaum.

Barton, M., Maruszewski, D., & Urrea, D. (1969). Variations of stimulus context and its effect on word finding ability in aphasics. *Cortex, 5,* 351–364.

Battig, W. F., & Montague, W. E. (1969). Category norms of verbal items in 56 categories: A replication and extension of the Connecticut category norms. *Journal of Experimental Psychology Monographs, 80*(3, Pt. 2).

Bruner, J. (1973). Development of equivalence transformations in children. In J. M. Anglin, *Beyond the information given* (pp. 352–367). New York: W. W. Norton.

Canter, G. (1972, November). *The nature of word-retrieval disturbances in aphasia.* Paper presented at the annual meeting of the American Speech and Hearing Association, San Francisco.

Clark, E. V. (1982). The young word maker: A case study of innovation in the child's lexicon. In E. Wanner & L. R. Gleitman (Eds.), *Language acquisition: The state of the art* (pp. 390–425). Cambridge, England: Cambridge University Press.

Coughlan, A. K., & Warrington, E. K. (1978). Word-comprehension and word retrieval in patients with localized cerebral lesions. *Brain, 101,* 163–185.

Denckla, M. B., & Rudel, R. (1976a). Naming of object drawings by dyslexic and other learning disabled children. *Brain and Language, 3,* 1–16.

Denckla, M. B., & Rudel, R. (1976b). Rapid "automatized" naming (R.A.N.): Dyslexia differentiated from other learning disabilities. *Neuropsychologia, 14,* 471–479.

Evens, M., Litowitz, B., Markowitz, J., Smith, R., & Werner, O. (1983). *Lexical-semantic relationships: A comparative survey.* Edmonton, Alberta, Canada: Linguistic Research.

Fried-Oken, M. B. (1984). *The development of naming skills in normal and language deficient children.* Unpublished doctoral dissertation, Boston University.

German, D. J. N. (1979). Word-finding skills in children with learning disabilities. *Journal of Learning Disabilities, 12,* 176–181.

German, D. J. N. (1982). Word-finding substitutions in children with learning disabilities. *Language, Speech, and Hearing Services in Schools, 13,* 223–230.

German, D. J. (1983). I know it but I can't think of it: Word retrieval difficulties. *Academic Therapy, 18,* 539–545.

German, D. J. (1984). Diagnosis of word-finding disorders in children with learning disabilities. *Journal of Learning Disabilities, 17,* 353–358.

German, D. J. (1985). The use of specific semantic word categories in the diagnosis of dysnomic learning disabled children. *British Journal of Disorders of Communication, 20,* 143–154.

German, D. J. ([1986] 1989). *National College of Education Test of Word Finding.* Allen, TX: DLM Teaching Resources.

German, D. J. (1987). Spontaneous language profiles of children with word finding problems. *Language, Speech and Hearing Services in the Schools, 18,* 217–230.

Goodglass, H., Klein, B., Carey, P., & Jones, K. (1966). Specific semantic word categories in aphasia. *Cortex, 2,* 74–89.

Goodglass, H., & Stuss, D. T. (1979). Naming to picture versus description in three aphasic subgroups. *Cortex, 15,* 199–211.

Halliday, M. A. K., & Hasan, R. (1976). *Cohesion in English.* London, England: Longman Group.

Halsey, W. D. (Editorial Director) & Morris, C. G. (Ed.). (1977). *Macmillan dictionary for children.* New York: Macmillan.

Hambleton, R. (1979). Latent trait models and their applications. In R. Traub (Ed.), *New directions for testing and measurement: Methodological developments* (pp. 13–32). San Francisco: Jossey-Bass.

Harris, A. J., & Jacobson, M. D. (1972). *Basic elementary reading vocabularies.* London, England: Macmillan, Collier Macmillan.

Hashway, R. M. (1978). *Objective mental measurement: Individual and program evaluation using the Rasch model.* New York: Praeger.

Helm, N. A. (1979). *The gestural behavior of aphasic patients during confrontation naming.* Unpublished doctoral dissertation, Boston University.

Johnson, D., & Myklebust, H. (1967). *Learning disabilities: Educational principles and practices.* New York: Grune & Stratton.

Johnson, K., Markert, L., Shuy, R. W., Squire, J. R., & Venezky, R. L. (1979). *Ginn basal readers. Grades K-6.* Lexington, MA: Ginn.

Kail, R., & Leonard, L. (1986). Word-finding abilities in language-impaired children. *ASHA Monographs, 25.*

Kaplan, E., Goodglass, H., & Weintraub, S. (1976). *Boston Naming Test (experimental ed.).* Boston: Veterans Administration Hospital.

Landau, C. (1988). [Construct validity of the TAWF.] Unpublished research data.

Leonard, L. B., Nippold, M. A., Kail, R., & Hale, C. A. (1983). Picture naming in language-impaired children: Differentiating lexical storage from retrieval. *Journal of Speech and Hearing Research, 26,* 609–615.

Luria, A. R. (1980). *Higher cortical functions in man* (rev. ed.) New York: Basic Books.

Lyons, J. (1977). *Semantics* (vol. 1). Cambridge, England: Cambridge University Press.

Miller, G., Galanter, E., & Pribram, K. (1960). *Plans and the structure of behavior.* New York: Holt, Rinehart & Winston.

Miller, G., & Johnson-Laird, P. (1976). *Language and perception.* Cambridge: Harvard University Press.

Morris, W. (Ed.). (1974). *The Ginn intermediate dictionary.* Middletown, CT: Ginn.

Norlin, P. (1981). The development of relational arcs in the lexical semantic memory structures of young children. *Journal of Child Language, 8,* 385–402.

Oldfield, R. C., & Wingfield, A. (1965). Response latencies in naming objects. *Quarterly Journal of Experimental Psychology, 17,* 273–281.

Riegel, K. F. (1970). The language acquisition process: A reinterpretation of selected research findings. In L. R. Goulet & P. B. Baltes (Eds.), *Life-span developmental psychology* (pp. 357–399). New York: Academic Press.

Rosch, E. (1975). Cognitive representations of semantic categories. *Journal of Experimental Psychology, 104*(3), 192–233.

Rosch, E. (1977). Classification of real-world objects: Origins and representations in cognition. In P. N. Johnson-Laird & P. C. Wason (Eds.), *Thinking: Readings in cognitive science* (pp. 212–222). Cambridge, England: Cambridge University Press.

Rosch, E., Mervis, C., Gray, W., Johnson, D., & Boyes-Braem, P. (1976). Basic objects in natural categories. *Cognitive Psychology, 8,* 382–439.

Rudel, R. G., Denckla, M. B., & Broman, M. (1981). The effect of varying stimulus context on word-finding ability: Dyslexia further differentiated from other learning disabilities. *Brain and Language, 13,* 130–144.

Rudel, R. G., Denckla, M. B., Broman, M., & Hirsch, S. (1980). Word-finding as a function of stimulus context: Children compared with aphasic adults. *Brain and Language, 10,* 111–119.

Rutherford, D., & Telser, E. (1967). *Word-finding abilities of kindergarten and first-grade children.* Paper presented at the annual meeting of the American Speech and Hearing Association, Chicago.

Salvia, J., & Ysseldyke, J. E. (1981). *Assessment in special and remedial education.* Boston: Houghton-Mifflin.

Schank, R. C., & Abelson, R. P. (1977). *Scripts, plans, goals and understanding.* Hillsdale, NJ: Lawrence Erlbaum.

Tulving, E. (1974). Cue dependent forgetting. *American Scientist. 62,* 74–82.

Vygotsky, L. (1986). *Thought and language.* (rev. ed.). Cambridge: M. I. T. Press.

Wiig, E. H., & Semel, E. M. (1976). *Language disabilities in children and adolescents.* Columbus, OH: Charles E. Merrill.

Wiig, E. H., & Semel, E. M. (1984). *Language assessment and intervention for the learning disabled* (rev. ed.). Columbus, OH: Charles E. Merrill.

Wiig, E. H., Semel, E. M., & Nystrom, L. A. (1982). Comparison of rapid naming abilities in language-learning-disabled and academically achieving eight-year-olds. *Language, Speech, and Hearing Services in the Schools, 13,* 11–23.

Wolf, M. (1980). The word-retrieval process and reading in children and aphasics. *Children's Language, 3,* 437–490.

Woodcock, R. W. (1973). *Woodcock Reading Mastery Tests.* Circle Pines, MN: American Guidance Service.

1 Norm Table 1
Standard Scores for Adolescents by Age Level

Total Raw Score	Standard Score	Standard Score SEM	Total Raw Score	Standard Score	Standard Score SEM
12–0 to 12–11 yrs			**13–0 to 13–11 yrs**		
<60	<65	4.23	<60	<65	4.23
60	65	4.23	60	65	4.23
61	66	4.23	61	66	4.23
62	67	4.23	62	67	4.23
63	68	4.23	63	68	4.23
64	69	4.23	64	69	4.23
65	69	4.23	65	69	4.23
66	70	4.23	66	70	4.23
67	71	4.23	67	71	4.23
68	72	4.23	68	72	4.23
69	73	4.23	69	73	4.23
70	74	4.23	70	74	4.23
71	75	4.23	71	75	4.23
72	76	4.42	72	76	4.42
73	77	4.42	73	77	4.42
74	78	4.42	74	78	4.42
75	79	4.42	75	79	4.42
76	80	4.42	76	80	4.42
77	81	4.42	77	81	4.42
78	83	4.62	78	83	4.62
79	84	4.62	79	84	4.62
80	85	4.62	80	85	4.62
81	86	4.62	81	86	4.62
82	87	4.81	82	87	4.81
83	88	4.81	83	88	4.81
84	90	4.81	84	90	4.81
85	91	5.00	85	91	5.00
86	92	5.00	86	92	5.00
87	93	5.00	87	93	5.00
88	95	5.19	88	95	5.19
89	96	5.19	89	96	5.19
90	98	5.38	90	98	5.38
91	99	5.58	91	99	5.58
92	101	5.58	92	101	5.58
93	103	5.77	93	103	5.77
94	105	5.96	94	105	5.96
95	107	6.15	95	107	6.15
96	109	6.35	96	109	6.35
97	111	6.54	97	111	6.54
98	113	6.92	98	113	6.92
99	116	7.31	99	116	7.31
100	119	7.69	100	119	7.69
101	122	8.27	101	122	8.27
102	126	9.04	102	126	9.04
103	131	10.00	103	131	10.00
104	137	11.35	104	137	11.35
105	145	13.85	105	145	13.85
106	159	19.42	106	159	19.42
107	173	21.30	107	173	21.30

Norm Table 1 (continued)
Standard Scores for Adolescents by Age Level

Total Raw Score	Standard Score	Standard Score SEM	Total Raw Score	Standard Score	Standard Score SEM
14–0 to 14–11 yrs			**15–0 to 15–11 yrs**		
<60	<61	4.23	<60	<57	4.23
60	61	4.23	60	57	4.23
61	62	4.23	61	58	4.23
62	63	4.23	62	59	4.23
63	64	4.23	63	60	4.23
64	65	4.23	64	61	4.23
65	66	4.23	65	62	4.23
66	67	4.23	66	63	4.23
67	68	4.23	67	64	4.23
68	69	4.23	68	65	4.23
69	70	4.23	69	66	4.23
70	71	4.23	70	66	4.23
71	72	4.23	71	67	4.23
72	73	4.42	72	68	4.42
73	74	4.42	73	69	4.42
74	75	4.42	74	70	4.42
75	76	4.42	75	72	4.42
76	77	4.42	76	73	4.42
77	78	4.42	77	74	4.42
78	79	4.62	78	75	4.62
79	80	4.62	79	76	4.62
80	81	4.62	80	77	4.62
81	82	4.62	81	78	4.62
82	84	4.81	82	79	4.81
83	85	4.81	83	80	4.81
84	86	4.81	84	82	4.81
85	87	5.00	85	83	5.00
86	89	5.00	86	84	5.00
87	90	5.00	87	86	5.00
88	91	5.19	88	87	5.19
89	93	5.19	89	89	5.19
90	94	5.38	90	90	5.38
91	96	5.58	91	92	5.58
92	98	5.58	92	93	5.58
93	99	5.77	93	95	5.77
94	101	5.96	94	97	5.96
95	103	6.15	95	99	6.15
96	105	6.35	96	101	6.35
97	107	6.54	97	103	6.54
98	110	6.92	98	105	6.92
99	112	7.31	99	108	7.31
100	115	7.69	100	111	7.69
101	119	8.27	101	115	8.27
102	123	9.04	102	119	9.04
103	128	10.00	103	123	10.00
104	134	11.35	104	129	11.35
105	142	13.85	105	138	13.85
106	156	19.42	106	152	19.42
107	170	21.30	107	166	21.30

Norm Table 1 (continued)
Standard Scores for Adolescents by Age Level

Total Raw Score	Standard Score	Standard Score SEM	Total Raw Score	Standard Score	Standard Score SEM
16–0 to 16–11 yrs			**17–0 to 19–11 yrs**		
<60	<57	4.23	<60	<55	4.23
60	57	4.23	60	55	4.23
61	58	4.23	61	56	4.23
62	59	4.23	62	57	4.23
63	60	4.23	63	57	4.23
64	61	4.23	64	58	4.23
65	62	4.23	65	59	4.23
66	63	4.23	66	60	4.23
67	64	4.23	67	61	4.23
68	65	4.23	68	62	4.23
69	66	4.23	69	63	4.23
70	66	4.23	70	64	4.23
71	67	4.23	71	65	4.23
72	68	4.42	72	66	4.42
73	69	4.42	73	67	4.42
74	70	4.42	74	68	4.42
75	72	4.42	75	69	4.42
76	73	4.42	76	70	4.42
77	74	4.42	77	71	4.42
78	75	4.62	78	72	4.62
79	76	4.62	79	73	4.62
80	77	4.62	80	75	4.62
81	78	4.62	81	76	4.62
82	79	4.81	82	77	4.81
83	80	4.81	83	78	4.81
84	82	4.81	84	79	4.81
85	83	5.00	85	81	5.00
86	84	5.00	86	82	5.00
87	86	5.00	87	83	5.00
88	87	5.19	88	85	5.19
89	89	5.19	89	86	5.19
90	90	5.38	90	88	5.38
91	92	5.58	91	89	5.58
92	93	5.58	92	91	5.58
93	95	5.77	93	93	5.77
94	97	5.96	94	94	5.96
95	99	6.15	95	96	6.15
96	101	6.35	96	98	6.35
97	103	6.54	97	101	6.54
98	105	6.92	98	103	6.92
99	108	7.31	99	106	7.31
100	111	7.69	100	109	7.69
101	115	8.27	101	112	8.27
102	119	9.04	102	116	9.04
103	123	10.00	103	121	10.00
104	129	11.35	104	127	11.35
105	138	13.85	105	135	13.85
106	152	19.42	106	149	19.42
107	166	21.30	107	163	21.30

2 Norm Table 2
Standard Scores for Adolescents by Grade Level

Total Raw Score	Standard Score	Standard Score SEM	Total Raw Score	Standard Score	Standard Score SEM
Grade 7			**Grade 8**		
<60	<66	4.23	<60	<63	4.23
60	66	4.23	60	63	4.23
61	67	4.23	61	64	4.23
62	68	4.23	62	65	4.23
63	69	4.23	63	66	4.23
64	70	4.23	64	67	4.23
65	71	4.23	65	68	4.23
66	72	4.23	66	69	4.23
67	73	4.23	67	70	4.23
68	74	4.23	68	71	4.23
69	75	4.23	69	72	4.23
70	76	4.23	70	73	4.23
71	77	4.23	71	74	4.23
72	78	4.42	72	75	4.42
73	79	4.42	73	76	4.42
74	80	4.42	74	77	4.42
75	81	4.42	75	78	4.42
76	82	4.42	76	79	4.42
77	83	4.42	77	80	4.42
78	84	4.62	78	81	4.62
79	85	4.62	79	83	4.62
80	87	4.62	80	84	4.62
81	88	4.62	81	85	4.62
82	89	4.81	82	86	4.81
83	90	4.81	83	87	4.81
84	91	4.81	84	89	4.81
85	93	5.00	85	90	5.00
86	94	5.00	86	91	5.00
87	96	5.00	87	93	5.00
88	97	5.19	88	94	5.19
89	98	5.19	89	96	5.19
90	100	5.38	90	97	5.38
91	102	5.58	91	99	5.58
92	103	5.58	92	100	5.58
93	105	5.77	93	102	5.77
94	107	5.96	94	104	5.96
95	109	6.15	95	106	6.15
96	111	6.35	96	108	6.35
97	113	6.54	97	110	6.54
98	116	6.92	98	113	6.92
99	119	7.31	99	116	7.31
100	122	7.69	100	119	7.69
101	125	8.27	101	122	8.27
102	129	9.04	102	126	9.04
103	134	10.00	103	131	10.00
104	140	11.35	104	137	11.35
105	149	13.85	105	146	13.85
106	163	19.42	106	160	19.42
107	177	21.30	107	175	21.30

Norm Table 2 (continued)
Standard Scores for Adolescents by Grade Level

Total Raw Score	Standard Score	Standard Score SEM	Total Raw Score	Standard Score	Standard Score SEM
Grade 9			**Grade 10**		
<60	<58	4.23	<60	<58	4.23
60	58	4.23	60	58	4.23
61	59	4.23	61	59	4.23
62	60	4.23	62	60	4.23
63	61	4.23	63	61	4.23
64	61	4.23	64	61	4.23
65	62	4.23	65	62	4.23
66	63	4.23	66	63	4.23
67	64	4.23	67	64	4.23
68	65	4.23	68	65	4.23
69	66	4.23	69	66	4.23
70	67	4.23	70	67	4.23
71	68	4.23	71	68	4.23
72	69	4.42	72	69	4.42
73	70	4.42	73	70	4.42
74	71	4.42	74	71	4.42
75	73	4.42	75	73	4.42
76	74	4.42	76	74	4.42
77	75	4.42	77	75	4.42
78	76	4.62	78	76	4.62
79	77	4.62	79	77	4.62
80	78	4.62	80	78	4.62
81	79	4.62	81	79	4.62
82	80	4.81	82	80	4.81
83	82	4.81	83	82	4.81
84	83	4.81	84	83	4.81
85	84	5.00	85	84	5.00
86	86	5.00	86	86	5.00
87	87	5.00	87	87	5.00
88	88	5.19	88	88	5.19
89	90	5.19	89	90	5.19
90	91	5.38	90	91	5.38
91	93	5.58	91	93	5.58
92	95	5.58	92	95	5.58
93	97	5.77	93	97	5.77
94	98	5.96	94	98	5.96
95	100	6.15	95	100	6.15
96	103	6.35	96	103	6.35
97	105	6.54	97	105	6.54
98	107	6.92	98	107	6.92
99	110	7.31	99	110	7.31
100	113	7.69	100	113	7.69
101	117	8.27	101	117	8.27
102	121	9.04	102	121	9.04
103	126	10.00	103	126	10.00
104	132	11.35	104	132	11.35
105	140	13.85	105	140	13.85
106	155	19.42	106	155	19.42
107	169	21.30	107	169	21.30

Norm Table 2 (continued)
Standard Scores for Adolescents by Grade Level

Total Raw Score	Standard Score	Standard Score SEM	Total Raw Score	Standard Score	Standard Score SEM
Grade 11			**Grade 12**		
<60	<56	4.23	<60	<51	4.23
60	56	4.23	60	51	4.23
61	56	4.23	61	52	4.23
62	57	4.23	62	53	4.23
63	58	4.23	63	54	4.23
64	59	4.23	64	55	4.23
65	60	4.23	65	56	4.23
66	61	4.23	66	57	4.23
67	62	4.23	67	58	4.23
68	63	4.23	68	59	4.23
69	64	4.23	69	60	4.23
70	65	4.23	70	61	4.23
71	66	4.23	71	62	4.23
72	67	4.42	72	63	4.42
73	68	4.42	73	64	4.42
74	69	4.42	74	65	4.42
75	70	4.42	75	66	4.42
76	71	4.42	76	67	4.42
77	73	4.42	77	68	4.42
78	74	4.62	78	69	4.62
79	75	4.62	79	70	4.62
80	76	4.62	80	71	4.62
81	77	4.62	81	73	4.62
82	78	4.81	82	74	4.81
83	80	4.81	83	75	4.81
84	81	4.81	84	76	4.81
85	82	5.00	85	78	5.00
86	83	5.00	86	79	5.00
87	85	5.00	87	80	5.00
88	86	5.19	88	82	5.19
89	88	5.19	89	83	5.19
90	89	5.38	90	85	5.38
91	91	5.58	91	86	5.58
92	93	5.58	92	88	5.58
93	94	5.77	93	90	5.77
94	96	5.96	94	92	5.96
95	98	6.15	95	94	6.15
96	100	6.35	96	96	6.35
97	103	6.54	97	98	6.54
98	105	6.92	98	101	6.92
99	108	7.31	99	103	7.31
100	111	7.69	100	106	7.69
101	114	8.27	101	110	8.27
102	119	9.04	102	114	9.04
103	123	10.00	103	119	10.00
104	130	11.35	104	125	11.35
105	138	13.85	105	134	13.85
106	153	19.42	106	148	19.42
107	167	21.30	107	162	21.30

3 Norm Table 3

Standard Scores for Adults by Age Level

Total Raw Score	Standard Score	Standard Score SEM	Total Raw Score	Standard Score	Standard Score SEM
20–0 to 39–11 yrs			**40–0 to 59–11 yrs**		
<60	<52	4.23	<60	<58	4.23
60	52	4.23	60	58	4.23
61	53	4.23	61	58	4.23
62	54	4.23	62	59	4.23
63	55	4.23	63	60	4.23
64	55	4.23	64	61	4.23
65	56	4.23	65	61	4.23
66	57	4.23	66	62	4.23
67	58	4.23	67	63	4.23
68	58	4.23	68	64	4.23
69	59	4.23	69	65	4.23
70	60	4.23	70	65	4.23
71	61	4.23	71	66	4.23
72	62	4.42	72	67	4.42
73	62	4.42	73	68	4.42
74	63	4.42	74	69	4.42
75	64	4.42	75	69	4.42
76	65	4.42	76	70	4.42
77	66	4.42	77	71	4.42
78	67	4.62	78	72	4.62
79	68	4.62	79	73	4.62
80	68	4.62	80	74	4.62
81	69	4.62	81	75	4.62
82	70	4.81	82	76	4.81
83	71	4.81	83	77	4.81
84	72	4.81	84	78	4.81
85	73	5.00	85	79	5.00
86	74	5.00	86	80	5.00
87	75	5.00	87	81	5.00
88	77	5.19	88	82	5.19
89	78	5.19	89	83	5.19
90	79	5.38	90	84	5.38
91	80	5.58	91	86	5.58
92	82	5.58	92	87	5.58
93	83	5.77	93	88	5.77
94	84	5.96	94	90	5.96
95	86	6.15	95	91	6.15
96	88	6.35	96	93	6.35
97	90	6.54	97	95	6.54
98	92	6.92	98	97	6.92
99	94	7.31	99	99	7.31
100	96	7.69	100	101	7.69
101	99	8.27	101	104	8.27
102	102	9.04	102	107	9.04
103	106	10.00	103	111	10.00
104	111	11.35	104	116	11.35
105	118	13.85	105	123	13.85
106	129	19.42	106	134	19.42
107	140	21.30	107	145	21.30

Norm Table 3 (continued)
Standard Scores for Adults by Age Level

Total Raw Score	Standard Score	Standard Score SEM
60–0 to 80–0 yrs		
<60	<70	4.23
60	70	4.23
61	70	4.23
62	71	4.23
63	72	4.23
64	73	4.23
65	73	4.23
66	74	4.23
67	75	4.23
68	76	4.23
69	76	4.23
70	77	4.23
71	78	4.23
72	79	4.42
73	80	4.42
74	80	4.42
75	81	4.42
76	82	4.42
77	83	4.42
78	84	4.62
79	85	4.62
80	86	4.62
81	87	4.62
82	88	4.81
83	89	4.81
84	90	4.81
85	91	5.00
86	92	5.00
87	93	5.00
88	94	5.19
89	95	5.19
90	96	5.38
91	98	5.58
92	99	5.58
93	100	5.77
94	102	5.96
95	103	6.15
96	105	6.35
97	107	6.54
98	109	6.92
99	111	7.31
100	113	7.69
101	116	8.27
102	119	9.04
103	123	10.00
104	128	11.35
105	135	13.85
106	146	19.42
107	157	21.30

4 Norm Table 4
Rasch Standard Errors of Measurement for TAWF-Ability Levels

Raw Scores	TAWF-Ability Level	Standard Error of Measurement
60	.30	.22
61	.34	.22
62	.39	.22
63	.44	.22
64	.48	.22
65	.53	.22
66	.58	.22
67	.63	.22
68	.68	.22
69	.72	.22
70	.77	.22
71	.82	.22
72	.87	.23
73	.93	.23
74	.98	.23
75	1.03	.23
76	1.08	.23
77	1.14	.23
78	1.19	.24
79	1.25	.24
80	1.30	.24
81	1.36	.24
82	1.42	.25
83	1.48	.25
84	1.55	.25
85	1.61	.26
86	1.68	.26
87	1.74	.26
88	1.81	.27
89	1.89	.27
90	1.96	.28
91	2.04	.29
92	2.13	.29
93	2.21	.30
94	2.31	.31
95	2.41	.32
96	2.51	.33
97	2.62	.34
98	2.75	.36
99	2.88	.38
100	3.03	.40
101	3.21	.43
102	3.41	.47
103	3.65	.52
104	3.95	.59
105	4.37	.72
106	5.08	1.01
107	5.79	1.11

5 Norm Table 5
Percentile Ranks for Adolescents by Age Level

Total Raw Score	Percentile Rank	Total Raw Score	Percentile Rank	Total Raw Score	Percentile Rank
12–0 to 12–11 yrs		**13–0 to 13–11 yrs**		**14–0 to 14–11 yrs**	
60	0.1	60	0.1	60	0.1
61	0.1	61	0.1	61	0.1
62	0.1	62	0.1	62	0.1
63	0.1	63	0.1	63	0.1
64	0.2	64	0.1	64	0.1
65	0.5	65	0.1	65	0.1
66	1.0	66	0.1	66	0.1
67	2.0	67	0.3	67	0.3
68	2.0	68	1.0	68	1.0
69	3.0	69	1.0	69	1.0
70	3.0	70	2.0	70	2.0
71	4.0	71	3.0	71	2.0
72	4.0	72	4.0	72	3.0
73	5.0	73	5.0	73	4.0
74	6.0	74	6.0	74	4.0
75	6.0	75	6.0	75	5.0
76	8.0	76	8.0	76	6.0
77	10.0	77	9.0	77	7.0
78	11.0	78	10.0	78	8.0
79	13.0	79	12.0	79	9.0
80	15.0	80	13.0	80	11.0
81	16.0	81	15.0	81	14.0
82	18.0	82	17.0	82	15.0
83	21.0	83	20.0	83	17.0
84	23.0	84	22.0	84	19.0
85	26.0	85	24.0	85	20.0
86	29.0	86	27.0	86	22.0
87	35.0	87	31.0	87	26.0
88	39.0	88	35.0	88	30.0
89	42.0	89	39.0	89	33.0
90	47.0	90	44.0	90	36.0
91	53.0	91	49.0	91	41.0
92	58.0	92	53.0	92	48.0
93	60.0	93	59.0	93	54.0
94	66.0	94	64.0	94	58.0
95	71.0	95	69.0	95	62.0
96	75.0	96	74.0	96	65.0
97	80.0	97	78.0	97	69.0
98	85.0	98	83.0	98	73.0
99	90.0	99	86.0	99	76.0
100	93.0	100	88.0	100	81.0
101	96.0	101	91.0	101	88.0
102	99.0	102	94.0	102	93.0
103	99.8	103	96.0	103	96.0
104	99.8	104	99.0	104	98.0
105	99.8	105	99.8	105	99.6
106	99.8	106	99.8	106	99.6
107	99.8	107	99.8	107	99.6

Norm Table 5 (Continued)
Percentile Ranks for Adolescents by Age Level

Total Raw Score	Percentile Rank	Total Raw Score	Percentile Rank	Total Raw Score	Percentile Rank
15–0 to 15–11 yrs		**16–0 to 16–11 yrs**		**17–0 to 19–11 yrs**	
60	0.1	60	0.1	60	0.1
61	0.1	61	0.1	61	0.1
62	0.1	62	0.1	62	0.1
63	0.1	63	0.1	63	0.1
64	0.1	64	0.1	64	0.1
65	0.1	65	0.1	65	0.1
66	0.1	66	0.1	66	0.1
67	0.1	67	0.1	67	0.1
68	0.3	68	0.1	68	0.1
69	0.6	69	0.1	69	0.1
70	1.0	70	0.1	70	0.1
71	2.0	71	0.1	71	0.1
72	2.0	72	0.3	72	0.3
73	2.0	73	1.0	73	1.0
74	3.0	74	3.0	74	2.0
75	4.0	75	4.0	75	3.0
76	5.0	76	4.0	76	3.0
77	6.0	77	5.0	77	4.0
78	6.0	78	5.0	78	4.0
79	7.0	79	6.0	79	5.0
80	8.0	80	7.0	80	6.0
81	9.0	81	8.0	81	7.0
82	11.0	82	9.0	82	8.0
83	12.0	83	10.0	83	9.0
84	13.0	84	12.0	83	10.0
85	15.0	85	13.0	85	12.0
86	18.0	86	15.0	86	15.0
87	19.0	87	17.0	87	17.0
88	22.0	88	20.0	88	18.0
89	25.0	89	22.0	89	21.0
90	29.0	90	25.0	90	24.0
91	32.0	91	28.0	91	26.0
92	36.0	92	32.0	92	29.0
93	41.0	93	35.0	93	33.0
94	45.0	94	40.0	94	39.0
95	49.0	95	45.0	95	44.0
96	54.0	96	50.0	96	48.0
97	59.0	97	57.0	97	52.0
98	66.0	98	63.0	98	58.0
99	73.0	99	70.0	99	65.0
100	79.0	100	78.0	100	71.0
101	85.0	101	84.0	101	78.0
102	90.0	102	89.0	102	85.0
103	95.0	103	93.0	103	90.0
104	98.0	104	97.0	104	95.0
105	99.5	105	98.0	105	97.0
106	99.5	106	99.5	106	99.3
107	99.5	107	99.5	107	99.5

6 Norm Table 6

Percentile Ranks for Adolescents by Grade Level

Total Raw Score	Percentile Rank	Total Raw Score	Percentile Rank	Total Raw Score	Percentile Rank
Grade 7		**Grade 8**		**Grade 9**	
60	0.2	60	0.1	60	0.1
61	0.4	61	0.1	61	0.1
62	0.8	62	0.2	62	0.1
63	1.0	63	0.3	63	0.1
64	1.0	64	0.4	64	0.1
65	2.0	65	0.6	65	0.1
66	2.0	66	0.7	66	0.1
67	2.0	67	0.8	67	0.3
68	2.0	68	1.0	68	0.5
69	3.0	69	1.0	69	0.8
70	3.0	70	2.0	70	1.0
71	3.0	71	2.0	71	2.0
72	4.0	72	3.0	72	2.0
73	5.0	73	4.0	73	3.0
74	7.0	74	4.0	74	3.0
75	9.0	75	4.0	75	3.0
76	11.0	76	6.0	76	3.0
77	12.0	77	7.0	77	4.0
78	14.0	78	8.0	78	6.0
79	17.0	79	10.0	79	6.0
80	18.0	80	12.0	80	7.0
81	20.0	81	15.0	81	9.0
82	23.0	82	16.0	82	13.0
83	25.0	83	18.0	83	16.0
84	27.0	84	20.0	84	17.0
85	29.0	85	23.0	85	17.0
86	33.0	86	26.0	86	18.0
87	37.0	87	31.0	87	21.0
88	41.0	88	36.0	88	25.0
89	44.0	89	41.0	89	28.0
90	49.0	90	45.0	90	30.0
91	56.0	91	49.0	91	34.0
92	61.0	92	53.0	92	39.0
93	65.0	93	59.0	93	44.0
94	69.0	94	65.0	94	48.0
95	74.0	95	70.0	95	53.0
96	79.0	96	74.0	96	57.0
97	83.0	97	77.0	97	61.0
98	87.0	98	81.0	98	68.0
99	90.0	99	85.0	99	75.0
100	92.0	100	89.0	100	81.0
101	95.0	101	93.0	101	88.0
102	97.0	102	96.0	102	93.0
103	99.0	103	98.0	103	96.0
104	99.7	104	99.2	104	98.0
105	99.8	105	99.4	105	99.2
106	99.8	106	99.7	106	99.7
107	99.9	107	99.8	107	99.8

Norm Table 6 (continued)
Percentile Ranks for Adolescents by Grade Level

Total Raw Score	Percentile Rank	Total Raw Score	Percentile Rank	Total Raw Score	Percentile Rank
Grade 10		**Grade 11**		**Grade 12**	
60	0.1	60	0.1	60	0.1
61	0.1	61	0.1	61	0.1
62	0.1	62	0.1	62	0.1
63	0.1	63	0.1	63	0.1
64	0.1	64	0.1	64	0.1
65	0.1	65	0.1	65	0.1
66	0.1	66	0.1	66	0.1
67	0.1	67	0.1	67	0.1
68	0.1	68	0.1	68	0.1
69	0.1	69	0.1	69	0.1
70	0.2	70	0.1	70	0.1
71	0.4	71	0.1	71	0.1
72	0.6	72	0.2	72	0.1
73	1.0	73	0.4	73	0.1
74	1.0	74	0.6	74	0.2
75	2.0	75	0.8	75	0.5
76	2.0	76	1.0	76	1.0
77	3.0	77	2.0	77	2.0
78	3.0	78	3.0	78	2.0
79	5.0	79	4.0	79	3.0
80	6.0	80	4.0	80	4.0
81	7.0	81	5.0	81	4.0
82	8.0	82	7.0	82	5.0
83	10.0	83	9.0	83	6.0
84	12.0	84	11.0	84	7.0
85	14.0	85	13.0	85	7.0
86	17.0	86	16.0	86	8.0
87	19.0	87	18.0	87	9.0
88	22.0	88	20.0	88	11.0
89	26.0	89	23.0	89	13.0
90	29.0	90	25.0	90	16.0
91	33.0	91	28.0	91	20.0
92	36.0	92	31.0	92	23.0
93	41.0	93	35.0	93	28.0
94	46.0	94	40.0	94	32.0
95	50.0	95	45.0	95	37.0
96	55.0	96	52.0	96	41.0
97	61.0	97	57.0	97	44.0
98	66.0	98	65.0	98	50.0
99	73.0	99	70.0	99	58.0
100	78.0	100	77.0	100	66.0
101	86.0	101	83.0	101	73.0
102	90.0	102	89.0	102	80.0
103	95.0	103	92.0	103	88.0
104	98.0	104	96.0	104	94.0
105	99.1	105	99.0	105	98.0
106	99.6	106	99.5	106	99.3
107	99.7	107	99.6	107	99.4

7 Norm Table 7

Percentile Ranks for Adults by Age Level

Total Raw Score	Percentile Rank	Total Raw Score	Percentile Rank	Total Raw Score	Percentile Rank
20–0 to 39–11 yrs		40–0 to 59–11 yrs		60–0 to 80–0 yrs	
60	0.1	60	0.1	60	1.0
61	0.1	61	0.1	61	1.0
62	0.1	62	0.1	62	2.0
63	0.1	63	0.1	63	2.0
64	0.1	64	0.1	64	2.0
65	0.1	65	0.1	65	2.0
66	0.1	66	0.1	66	3.0
67	0.1	67	0.2	67	3.0
68	0.1	68	0.3	68	4.0
69	0.1	69	0.4	69	4.0
70	0.1	70	0.6	70	4.0
71	0.1	71	0.8	71	5.0
72	0.1	72	1.0	72	6.0
73	0.2	73	1.0	73	7.0
74	0.3	74	2.0	74	8.0
75	0.5	75	2.0	75	8.0
76	0.7	76	2.0	76	9.0
77	1.0	77	2.0	77	11.0
78	1.0	78	3.0	78	12.0
79	2.0	79	3.0	79	13.0
80	2.0	80	4.0	80	15.0
81	2.0	81	4.0	81	17.0
82	2.0	82	5.0	82	19.0
83	3.0	83	6.0	83	21.0
84	4.0	84	6.0	84	23.0
85	4.0	85	7.0	85	25.0
86	5.0	86	8.0	86	27.0
87	5.0	87	10.0	87	31.0
88	6.0	88	11.0	88	36.0
89	7.0	89	14.0	89	40.0
90	9.0	90	15.0	90	43.0
91	10.0	91	16.0	91	46.0
92	12.0	92	18.0	92	49.0
93	16.0	93	21.0	93	52.0
94	19.0	94	24.0	94	56.0
95	21.0	95	28.0	95	60.0
96	24.0	96	32.0	96	64.0
97	27.0	97	36.0	97	69.0
98	30.0	98	42.0	98	73.0
99	34.0	99	49.0	99	80.0
100	41.0	100	57.0	100	85.0
101	50.0	101	64.0	101	90.0
102	59.0	102	71.0	102	94.0
103	69.0	103	79.0	103	96.0
104	80.0	104	88.0	104	98.0
105	87.0	105	94.0	105	98.0
106	93.0	106	97.0	106	99.3
107	98.0	107	99.3	107	99.5

APPENDIX A

Figure A-1. Sample completed TAWF *Response Booklet*

NATIONAL COLLEGE OF EDUCATION

RESPONSE BOOKLET

TEST OF ADOLESCENT/ADULT WORD FINDING

TAWF

Diane J. German, Ph.D.

Name Art Example

School Lincoln Senior High Grade 10

Examiner Judy Katz

Teacher Donna Lynn

Referred by Ethel Newman

Address 613 S. Michigan St.

Geoffry, IL Phone 123-4567

Parent/Guardian/Spouse/Caretaker Eva + Ben Example

	Year	Month	Day
Test Date	88 ~~89~~	12+4=16	10
(−) Birthdate	72	8	6
(=) Age	16	8	4*

*If the number of days exceeds 15, add a month to the age.

☐ Brief Test

☒ Complete Test

If following up the Brief Test with the complete test, record the complete test results in a different color.

Accuracy Score Summary

Raw Score

Section	Brief Test	Complete Test
1. Picture Naming: Nouns		23
2. Sentence Completion Naming		12
3. Description Naming		9
4. Picture Naming: Verbs		13
5. Category Naming		17
TOTAL RAW SCORE		74

Scores Based on ☐ Age ☒ Grade

	Brief Test	Complete Test
Standard Score (SS)	(Table 5-1, 5-2, or 5-3)	71 (Norm Table 1, 2, or 3)
Standard Error of Measurement (SEM)	(Table 5-1, 5-2, or 5-3)	4.42 (Norm Table 1, 2, or 3)
Range of Confidence (SS − 1 and + 1 SEM)	to	67 to 75
Percentile Rank	(Table 5-5, 5-6, or 5-7)	1 (Norm Table 5, 6, or 7)

Plot the SS on the Word Finding Profile *(page 8)*.

Comprehension Summary *(from page 7)*

HIGH ☒ Percent of comprehension is high.

LOW ☐ Percent of comprehension is low. *(Refer to Prorated Accuracy Rescoring Procedure on page 7.)*

Item Response Time Summary *(Section 1, Picture Naming: Nouns)*

Estimated Item Response Time (ERT) (Number of Delayed Responses — 4 Seconds or More), Brief Test = ______

Estimated Item Response Time (ERT) (Number of Delayed Responses — 4 Seconds or More), Complete Test = 10

Total Item Response Time, Complete Test = 130 / 77 (in seconds/hundredths)

Average Item Response Time (ART), Complete Test = Total Item Response Time/37 = 3 / 53 (in seconds/hundredths)

Plot the ERT or the ART on the Word Finding Profile *(page 8)*.

Word Finding Profile

Profile A: ☐ Fast and inaccurate namer

Profile B: ☐ Slow and inaccurate namer

Profile C: ☐ Fast and accurate namer

Profile D: ☐ Slow and accurate namer

DLM
One DLM Park • Allen, Texas 75002

1

Section 1
Picture Naming: Nouns

Starter Items A. nose B. thumb C. kite D. whistle

Item	1 or 0		Subject's Response	Item Response Time			Ges. (✓)	Ex. Ver. (✓)	Comprehension		Response Code (after testing)
				☒ Estimated During Testing		☒ Actual from Tape Recording (sec/hun) (after testing)					
	Brief Test	Complete Test		Less Than 4 sec. (✓)	More Than 4 sec. (✓)				Yes (✓)	No	
1. ruler		1		✓		1 / 04					
2. mask		1			✓	4 / 16					
3. antenna		1		✓		1 / 90					
4. statue		0	man on a horse		✓	5 / 98			✓		C (VS)
5. crutch		1		✓		2 / 46					
6. suspenders		1		✓		2 / 16					
7. calculator		0	computer	✓		2 / 75			✓		CO
8. palm		1		✓		1 / 25					
9. microphone		1		✓		1 / 37					
10. dice		1		✓		1 / 36					
11. chopsticks		1		✓		3 / 35					
12. battery		0	box		✓	8 / 26			✓		VS
13. eyebrow		1		✓		1 / 25					
14. binoculars		1			✓	12 / 15	✓				
15. dart		1		✓		2 / 20					
16. magnet		1		✓		3 / 19					
17. acorn		0	fruit		✓	5 / 12			✓		CH
18. igloo		1		✓		1 / 42					
19. starfish		0	shellfish	✓		2 / 40			✓		PA
20. film		0	tape	✓		2 / 69			✓		VS
21. backpack		1		✓		2 / 49					
22. unicorn		1		✓		1 / 35					
23. harmonica		1		✓		2 / 46					
24. wishbone		0	I don't know		✓	15 / 80			✓		NR
25. propeller		1		✓		3 / 10					
26. jack		0	lifter		✓	6 / 59	✓		✓		FA
27. thimble		1		✓		2 / 16					
28. compass		0	directions	✓		2 / 42			✓		FA
29. funnel		0	siphon		✓	5 / 27			✓		CO
30. pliers		0	wrench	✓		1 / 88			✓		CO
31. dustpan		1		✓		2 / 86					
32. hopscotch		1		✓		1 / 88					
33. blimp		1			✓	4 / 78					
34. thermos		0	coffee cup	✓		2 / 28	✓		✓		PW
35. tambourine		0	drum	✓		2 / 20			✓		CO
36. spatula		1		✓		2 / 16	✓				
37. seahorse		0	dragon fish		✓	5 / 43			✓		VS

Brief Test Raw Score	RAW SCORE	Total Delayed Items	Total Item Response Time	Ges. Total	Ex. Ver. Total	Comprehension Total
	23	10	130/77	4	0	0 (total unknown)

2

Section 2
Sentence Completion Naming

Starter Items

A. A bird lays eggs in a (nest).
B. An instructor of a football team is the football (coach).
C. The outer part of an apple pie is the pie• (crust).
D. The net-like structure that a spider weaves is a spider (web).

Item	1 or 0		Subject's Response	Gesture (✓)	Extra Verbal (✓)	Sentence Comp[1] Yes (✓)	No	Word Comp Yes (✓)	No	Comp Summary Yes (✓)	No	Response Code
	Brief Test	Complete Test										
1. When you ride a horse, you sit on a leather (saddle).		1										
2. Hot melted rock flowing from an active volcano is called (lava).		1										
3. The officer showed his sheriff's (badge).		1										
4. A scientist looks at small things through a (microscope).		1										
5. You walk a dog with a leather (leash).		1										
6. The library book is kept on the book• (shelf).		1										
7. It's fun to shake a friendly dog's front (paw).		0	I don't know			✓		✓		✓		NR
8. A paper that indicates that you completed high school is your high school (diploma).		1										
9. When you hold a rose, you can prick your finger on a (thorn).		0	pricker	✓		✓		✓		✓		FA
10. To grow a vegetable in a garden, you plant a (seed).		1										
11. The highest point of a mountain is the (peak).		1										
12. A round model of the earth is a (globe).		0	sun	✓		✓		✓		✓		A
13. A person who rides racehorses is called a (jockey).		0	race horse driver			✓		✓		✓		C (FA)
14. To study the stars you look through a (telescope).		1										
15. A gentle song used to put babies to sleep is a (lullaby).		1										
16. The space between rows of seats is the (aisle)		1										

Brief Test Raw Score	RAW SCORE	Gesture Total	Extra Verbal Total	Comprehension Total (total unknown)
	12	2	0	0

[1] Subject must receive a "Yes" for sentence *and* word comprehension to score "Yes" on summary. All other combinations receive a "No" on summary.

3

Section 3
Description Naming

Starter Items

A. What is used for a bird's home, is made of small pieces of grass, and is found in a tree? (nest)

B. What do you find at the beach, is soft to walk on, and is used to build play castles? (sand)

C. What part of your face is used for eating, has teeth and a tongue, and is below your nose? (mouth)

D. What do you put on an envelope, is rectangular or square, and has glue on the back? (stamp)

Item	1 or 0 Brief Test	1 or 0 Complete Test	Subject's Response	Gesture (✓)	Extra Verbal (✓)	Sentence Comp[1] Yes (✓)	Sentence Comp[1] No	Word Comp Yes (✓)	Word Comp No	Comp Summary Yes (✓)	Comp Summary No	Response Code
1. What gives people a warning, is used on police cars and fire trucks, and makes a loud noise? (siren)		1										
2. What is a hat that is made of a hard material and is used to protect the head when playing football? (helmet)		1										
3. What is a permanent picture that is drawn on your skin by putting color in with a needle? (tattoo)		1										
4. What is a moving stairway that is found in a department store and that takes people up and down? (escalator)		1										
5. What is the name of a group of people chosen in court to hear evidence and give a verdict in a trial? (jury)		1										
6. What is a machine that may be shaped like a person and is programmed to do certain human jobs? (robot)		0	Um, I can't think		✓	✓		✓		✓		NR
7. What do you plant in the ground that is small and hard and that grows into a flower or vegetable? (seed)		1										
8. What is the kind of clothing that is funny or strange and is worn on stage or for a special party? (costume)		0	tuxedo	✓		✓		✓		✓		PW
9. What is the imaginary circle around the earth halfway between the North and South Poles? (equator)		1										
10. What is a large covered basket often found in your bedroom or bathroom in which you put dirty clothes? (hamper)		1										
11. What is the name of the hair that is cut short and brushed down over the forehead? (bangs)		1										
12. What is a long paddle made of wood that is used to move a boat through the water? (oar)		0	long flat thing	✓		✓		✓		✓		C (VS)

Brief Test Raw Score	RAW SCORE	Gesture Total	Extra Verbal Total	Comprehension Total (total unknown)
	9	2	1	0

[1]Subject must receive a "Yes" for sentence *and* word comprehension to score "Yes" on summary. All other combinations receive a "No" on summary.

4

Section 4
Picture Naming: Verbs

Starter Items

A. knocking	B. catching	C. diving	D. packing

Item	1 or 0 Brief Test	1 or 0 Complete Test	Subject's Response	Gesture (✓)	Extra Verbal (✓)	Comprehension Yes (✓)	Comprehension No	Response Code
1. dancing		1						
2. licking		1						
3. pulling		1						
4. squeezing		1						
5. dripping		1						
6. rolling		1						
7. drilling		1						
8. measuring		1						
9. marching		1						
10. braiding		0	fixing			✓		AV
11. winking		0	crying			✓		AV
12. plugging		1						
13. filing		1						
14. weighing		1						
15. grating		0	I don't know; cutting	✓	✓	✓		COV
16. begging		0	standing			✓		PWV
17. threading		0	sewing	✓		✓		SUPV
18. knitting		0	weaving	✓		✓		COV
19. parachuting		0	sky diving			✓		COV
20. directing		1						
21. developing		0	um, filming			✓		AV

Brief Test Raw Score	RAW SCORE	Gesture Total	Extra Verbal Total	Comprehension Total (total unknown)
	13	3	1	0

5

Section 5
Category Naming

Starter Items

A. birds B. candy C. days D. music

Item	1 or 0 Brief Test	1 or 0 Complete Test	Subject's Response	Gesture (✓)	Extra Verbal (✓)	Comprehension Yes (✓)	Comprehension No	Response Code
1. holidays		1						
2. states		1						
3. time		1						
4. presidents		1						
5. oceans		1						
6. rivers		1						
7. planets		1						
8. dances		1						
9. religions		0	beliefs			✓		FA
10. seasons		1						
11. silverware		1						
12. directions		1						
13. countries		1						
14. senses		1						
15. cities		1						
16. transportation		1						
17. metals		1						
18. appliances		1						
19. awards		0	trophies			✓		R
20. organs		0	body parts			✓		C (LA)
21. punctuation		0	I can't think of it		1	✓		NR

Brief Test Raw Score	RAW SCORE	Gesture Total	Extra Verbal Total	Comprehension Total (total unknown)
	17	0	1	0

6

Informal Assessment of Word Finding

Comprehension Summary

	Total Words		Unknown Words		Known Words		Total Words		
Brief Test	40	−		=		÷	40	=	%
Complete Test	107	−	0	=	107	÷	107	=	100 %

Percent of Comprehension

☒ 90% or above = HIGH comprehension on TAWF
☐ 89% or below = LOW comprehension on TAWF (Use Prorated Accuracy Rescoring Procedure)

Prorated Accuracy Rescoring Summary

	Raw Score from Accuracy Score Summary		Known Words from Comprehension Summary		Percent of Known Words Named Correctly	Prorated Accuracy Raw Score (Table G-1)
Brief Test		÷		=	%	
Complete Test		÷		=	%	

Prorated Scores Based on ☐ Age ☐ Grade

	Brief Test	Complete Test
Prorated Accuracy Standard Score	Table 5-1, 5-2, or 5-3	Norm Table 1, 2, or 3
Standard Error of Measurement	Table 5-1, 5-2, or 5-3	Norm Table 1, 2, or 3
Range of Confidence (SS − 1 and + 1 SEM)	to	to
Prorated Accuracy Percentile Rank	Table 5-5, 5-6, or 5-7	Norm Table 5, 6, or 7

Gestures and Extra Verbalizations Summary

Section	Number of Items with Gestures	Number of Items with Extra Verbalizations
1. Picture Naming: Nouns	4	0
2. Sentence Completion Naming	2	0
3. Description Naming	2	1
4. Picture Naming: Verbs	3	1
5. Category Naming	0	1

	Gestures (sum)		Percent of Items	Extra Verbalizations (sum)		Percent of Items
Brief Test		÷ 40 =	%		÷ 40 =	%
Complete Test	11	÷ 107 =	10 %	3	÷ 107 =	3 %

Substitution Type Summary *(sections 1, 2, 3, and 5)*

Record from response code columns in sections 1, 2, 3, and 5, or use Appendix D, Figure D-1.

Type	Number	Type	Number	Type	Number
SUP		CH	1	PW	2
CO	4	PA	1	IN	
SUB		IS		GN	
FA	4	R	1	UN	
LA		AA		C	4
COM		VS	3	SC	
A	1	VP		NR	4

Substitution Type Summary *(section 4)*

Record from response code column in section 4, or use Appendix D, Figure D-2.

Type	Number	Type	Number	Type	Number
SUPV	1	CH		PWV	1
COV	3	PAV		PL	
SUBV		ISV		IV	
PVA		RWV		CV	
RN		VSV		SC	
AV	3	VP		NR	

7

Word Finding Profile
Accuracy and Time Chart

Name *Art Example* Grade/~~Age~~ *10* Test Date *4/10/89*

Circle the subject's Estimated Item Response Time (ERT) in the top section or the Average Item Response Time (ART) in the bottom section. Then, in the middle grid, shade in the intersection of either of the ERT or ART measure and the subject's Accuracy Standard Score. Check the appropriate Word Finding Profile on page 1.

Estimated Item Response Time (ERT)

ERT = *10* (Delayed responses — 4 seconds or longer)

Based on ☐ Brief Test
☒ Complete Test

1. ERT cutoff (darker shading) for each grade or age level is the number of delayed responses (4 seconds or longer) representing the slowest 20% of the group at that grade or age level in the standardization sample. Borderline ranges are represented by the lighter shading.

BRIEF TEST	**Grade** 7- 8		0	1	2	3	4	>4
	9-12		0	1	2	3	4	>4
	Age 12-13		0	1	2	3	4	>4
	14-19		0	1	2	3	4	>4
	20-39		0	1	2	3	4	>4
	40-59		0	1	2	3	4	>4
	60-80	0	1	2	3	4	5	>5
COMPLETE TEST	**Grade** 7- 8	<3	3	4	5	6	7	>7
	9-12	<2	2	3	4	5	6	(>6)
	Age 12-13	<3	3	4	5	6	7	>7
	14-19	<2	2	3	4	5	6	>6
	20-39	0	1	2	3	4	5	>5
	40-59	<2	2	3	4	5	6	>6
	60-80	<5	5	6	7	8	9	>9

Accuracy Standard Score

Accuracy Standard Score = *71*

Based on ☒ Grade
☐ Age

Based on ☐ Brief Test
☒ Complete Test

2. Accuracy cutoff (darker shading) is 1 SD below the mean Accuracy Standard Score. Borderline ranges (lighter shading) represent a ± 1 SEM confidence interval (68% level) around the Accuracy cutoff.

Score							
<65							
65							
66							
67							
68							
69							
70							
71							
72							
73							
74							
75	**A** FAST AND						**B** SLOW AND
76	INACCURATE						INACCURATE
77	NAMER						NAMER
78							
79							
80							
81							
82							
83							
84							
85							
86							
87							
88							
89							
90							
91							
92	**C** FAST AND						**D** SLOW AND
93	ACCURATE						ACCURATE
94	NAMER						NAMER
95							
96							
97							
98							
99							
100							
101							
102							
103							
104							
105							
106							
107							
108							
109							
110							
111							
112							
113							
114							
115							
>115							

Average Item Response Time (ART)

ART = _____/_____ (seconds/hundredths)

3. ART cutoff (darker shading) is 1 SD above the mean Average Item Response Time for each grade or age level. Borderline ranges (lighter shading) represent ± 1 SEM confidence interval (68% level) around the ART cutoff. Use ART for the complete TAWF only.

COMPLETE TEST	**Grade** 7-12		0	1	2	3	4	>4
	Age 12-19		0	1	2	3	4	>4
	20-39		0	1	2	3	4	>4
	40-59		0	1	2	3	4	>4
	60-80	0	1	2	3	4	5	>5

8

J081A Printed in U.S.A.

APPENDIX B

Acceptable Substitutions and Errors for Target Words

B Table B-1
Acceptable Substitutions and Errors for Target Words in Section 1, Picture Naming: Nouns

Target Word	Acceptable Substitutions	Errors
1. ruler		meterstick, measurer, tape measurer
2. mask	eye mask	spectacles, eyeglasses, eyes, blindfold, masquerade
3. antenna	aerial, t.v. antenna	television, t.v. monitor, telephone, satellite, t.v.
4. statue	monument	horse, sculpture, man and horse
5. crutch	crutches	cane, third leg, cane stick
6. suspenders	braces	straps, man, overalls, belts, boy
7. calculator		adding machine, typewriter, computer, machine, digital
8. palm	palm of hand	hand, arm
9. microphone	mike	speaker, microscope, voice piece
10. dice	die	numbers, pips, checkers, dominoes
11. chopsticks		sticks, Chinese fork, tongs, Japanese, Chinese
12. battery	small battery	gasoline, generator, dry cell, terminal, radio, tank
13. eyebrow		eyelash, eyelid, brow, hair, eyes
14. binoculars	field glasses	microscope, goggles, specs, eyeglasses, camera, opera glasses, sky watchers
15. dart		rocket, arrow, target, needle, ice pick, spear
16. magnet		horseshoe, "U", magnetic, shoe
17. acorn		clove, nut, Capricorn, walnut, chestnut, unicorn, mushroom, corn
18. igloo		iceberg, ice, icicles, Eskimo (house), ice house, hut, tunnel, cabin, shed
19. starfish		star, shell, fish, sea star, sea fish, seashell, urchin, sand dollar, sea star, catfish
20. film	roll of film, filmstrip	picture, tape, movie screen, slide
21. backpack	knapsack	back sack, pack, bag, handbag, camping gear, vest, carrier, book bag, knit bag, carrier
22. unicorn		hair, horse, horsehead, mane, Cape Cod, hair-a-corn, horn horse
23. harmonica	mouth organ	whistle, french harp, music, violin, monica
24. wishbone	pulley bone	bone, drumstick, luck thing, food, chicken leg, leg bone, plate, fish bone
25. propeller		windmill, airplane, props, blades, fan, motor, wings
26. jack		clamp, kickstand, wedge, crane, wrench clamp, pump, tool, pulley, jackhammer, car jack, lever, (hydraulic) lift
27. thimble		thumbtack, thermos, thumb, acorn, nimble, thumble, finger cup
28. compass		clock, directions, direction thingy, gauge, barometer, stopwatch, rim, weathervane, campus

B Table B-1 (continued)
Acceptable Substitutions and Errors for Target Words in Section 1, Picture Naming: Nouns

Target Word	Acceptable Substitutions	Errors
29. funnel		oil filter, cylinder, drainer, tool, flask, horn, oil, filter, pourer, siphon, tunnel
30. pliers		wrench, tool, screwdriver, nutcrackers, tweezers, pincher
31. dustpan		dishpan, shovel, tray, pan, dirt pan, scooper, dust tray, duster, scraper, waste pan, sweeper
32. hopscotch	hopscotch game	number steps, board, number, tic tactor, game, edge, jumping, puzzle, outside
33. blimp	dirigible, zeppelin, Goodyear blimp	airship, Hindenberg, hot air balloon, airplane, balloon, aircraft, submarine, weather
34. thermos	lunch thermos, thermos jug, thermos bottle	tea pot, coffee pot, coffee holder, coffee mug, mug, pot, pitcher, coffee maker, can, thermal, percolator
35. tambourine		drum, banjo, cymbals, jamborine, baton, instrument, trampoline, tangerine, jingle-jingle, bell
36. spatula		knife, mixer, instrument spreader, rubber scraper, cake spreader, cake mixer, scraper thing, stirrer, strainer, spoon, rubber spoon, spade, butter knife, butter spreader
37. seahorse		Scorpio, sea monster, horse, starfish, horse fish, alligator, fish, sea fish, sea lion, Charley horse, iguana, dragon, swordfish, shellfish

B Table B-2
Acceptable Substitutions and Errors for Target Words in Section 2, Sentence Completion Naming

Target Word	Acceptable Substitutions	Errors
1. saddle		harness, back, bridle, straddle, seat
2. lava	magma	eruption, lather, molten, larva, coal, volcanic ash
3. badge		office, I.D., tickets, sheriff licence, guns, star, identification
4. microscope		telescope binoculars, magnifying glasses, scope, magnifier, stethoscope
5. leash		harness, lead, muzzle, collar, chain, strap, belt
6. shelf	bookshelf	rack library number, cover, stand, card, cart, record, case, file, list
7. paw		coat, throat, hair, ear, leg, fur, feet, chair, teeth, tail, back
8. diploma		G.E.D., equivalency test, scholarship, grad, graduation, S.A.T., record, certification, certificate, education, report card, exam, degree, transcript
9. thorn		sticker, petal, stone, stem, needle, bud, pricker, prick, plant, thumb, pin, point
10. seed		bulb, garden, crop, vegetable, carrot, tomato, food, root, sow, farm, row, fruit

Table B-2 (continued)
Acceptable Substitutions and Errors for Target Words in Section 2, Sentence Completion Naming

Target Word	Acceptable Substitutions	Errors
11. peak	summit, apex	plateau, edge, point, tip, top, cliff, climax, crest, pike, highest
12. globe		atmosphere, circle, atlas, map, model, planet, sphere
13. jockey		jock, horse rider, race, racer, derby, equestrian
14. telescope		microscope, binoculars, scope, periscope, micro
15. lullaby		melody, nursery rhyme, bedtime, rock-a-bye, fairy song, hymn, rock-a-bye-baby, carol, bedtime story, ballad, harmony
16. aisle		armrest, walkway, distance, bleachers, alley, dirt, floor, passage, walk space, row, seat, space, columns, furrow, space, irrigation

Table B-3
Acceptable Substitutions and Errors for Target Words in Section 3, Description Naming

Target Word	Acceptable Substitutions	Errors
1. siren		fire engine, horn, lights, signal, alarm, warning
2. helmet	football helmet	hard hat, cap, gloves, baseball hat, fiberglass
3. tattoo		stitch, birthmark, shot, graft, blood, embroidery
4. escalator		elevators, electric stairs
5. jury		lawyers, judge, suspect, court, witness, counsel, jurors
6. robot	android	computer, telescope, machine
7. seed	plant seed, bulb	plant, bud, branch
8. costume		clown, suit, dress-up clothes, gown, hats, mask, polka dots, armor, clown suit, tuxedo
9. equator		meridian, continental divide, circumference, hemisphere, atmosphere, sphere, axis, primal ridge, atlas, arctic, eclipse, ozone, time zone, earth
10. hamper	clothes hamper	bassinet, clothes basket, laundry, basket, clothes bin, pail, wastebasket, pantry, wicker basket
11. bangs		fringe, toupee, hairline, flattop, colic, hair, bob, eyebrow, style, crew cut, scalp, layered cut, beard
12. oar		paddle, motor, paddle wheel, rudder, canoe, row, sail, propeller

Table B-4
Acceptable Substitutions and Errors for Target Words in Section 4, Picture Naming: Verbs

Target Word	Acceptable Substitutions	Errors
1. dancing	dance	playing, fighting, boxing
2. licking	lick	eating, tasting, tongue, drinking
3. pulling	pull	breaking, tearing, yanking, weeding, tugging, picking, raking

B Table B-4 (continued)
Acceptable Substitutions and Errors for Target Words in Section 4, Picture Naming: Verbs

Target Word	Acceptable Substitutions	Errors
4. squeezing	squeeze, lemon squeezing	squirting, dipping, lemons, cleaning, spilling
5. dripping	drip	leaking, drop, water, running, faucet, dipping
6. rolling	roll, rolling dough	flattening, smoothing, baking, doughing, kneading
7. drilling	drill	screwing, sewing, shoot, driving, boring, riveting
8. measuring	measure	standing, getting measurements, looking, leaning, checking, height, sizing, growing, writing, drawing
9. marching	march	holding, walking, parading, band
10. braiding	plaiting, braid	twisting, knotting, tying, rolling hair, curling, weaving
11. winking	wink	blinking, frowning, looking, smiling
12. plugging	plug in, unplugging, plug	putting, pushing, push, inserting, connecting, current, sticking
13. filing	file	organizing, drawing, putting in, finding, taking, storing, pulling, file, inserting, desk, research
14. weighing	weigh	wading, looking, leaning, bending, scaling, standing, watching
15. grating	shredding, grate	grinding, scraping, chopping, rubbing, cutting, peeling, shearing, slicing, scrubbing
16. begging	beg	panhandling, charity, greeting, asking, bowing, holding, dying, wanting, giving, handling, pleading
17. threading	thread	sewing, stitching, fitting, tying, sticking, stringing, poking, eyeing, needling
18. knitting	knit	yarning, sewing, threading, weaving, meaning, crocheting
19. parachuting	parachute	jumping, flying, falling, floating, skydiving, ballooning
20. directing	direct	waving, controlling, signaling, stopping, policing, trafficking, officering, whistling
21. developing	develop	dunking, filming, producing, processing, rinsing, scooping, preparing, dipping, removing, wetting, getting, washing, photographing

B Table B-5
Acceptable Substitutions and Errors for Target Words in Section 5, Category Naming

Target Word	Acceptable Substitutions	Errors
1. holidays		vacations, celebrations, days off, festivals, months, seasons
2. states		oceans, countries, cities
3. time	time element, time of day	week, hours, days, clock
4. presidents		monuments, cities, memorial, people, birthdays, statues, politicians
5. oceans		rivers, places, seas, lakes, water, capital, people, great

B Table B-5
Acceptable Substitutions and Errors for Target Words in Section 5, Category Naming

Target Word	Acceptable Substitutions	Errors
6. rivers		states, lakes, water, countries, bodies, places
7. planets		universe, stars, satellites, comets, solar system, galaxy, space, universe, Mars
8. dances	dancing	waltz, steps, moves, exercise
9. religions	faiths, denominations	Christians, churches, belief, culture, priest
10. seasons		weather, months, times of the year, fall, time zone
11. silverware	utensils, cutlery, tableware, flatware	utility, apparel, tools, stencil, dishes, plate, eating
12. directions		North, West, places, poles, geographic locations, hemispheres, places, compass
13. countries	nations	communities, continents, communists, states, Europe
14. senses		feelings, signs, actions, body functions, sensitive areas
15. cities	towns, major city	places, states, capitals, countries, monuments, crowd
16. transportation	vehicles, conveyances	automobiles, vehicle, travel, traveling, traffic, carriers, rides
17. metals		minerals, ore, resources, steels, conductors, elements, solids
18. appliances		devices, aids, equipment, machines, artifacts, kitchen utensils, ranges, hardware, furniture
19. awards		rewards, honors, prizes, medallions, trophies, sports, plaques, gifts
20. organs	human organs, internal organs	intestines, parts, parts of the body, insides, human, muscles, tissue, flesh
21. punctuation	punctuation marks	marks, signs, pronunciation, quotations, parts of speech, symbols, English, endings, usage, quotations, decimal, comma

APPENDIX C

Classifications of Typical Target-Word Substitutions

C Table C-1
Suggested Classifications of Typical Target-Word Substitutions on the TAWF—Section 1, Picture Naming: Nouns

Target Word	Substitution	Classification
1. ruler	tape	Coordinate (CO)
	yardstick	Subordinate (SUB)
	measuring thing, measuring tape	Circumlocution (C) [Functional Attribute (FA)]
	scale	Coordinate (CO)
	rule	Phonemic Attribute (PA)
	measure	Functional Attribute (FA)
2. mask	eye mask	Acceptable Substitution (AS)
	shades	Chained (CH)
	eyeglass, glasses	Visual Substitution (VS)
	eye cover, false face	Circumlocution (C) [Functional Attribute (FA)]
	face mask	Subordinate (SUB)
	blindfold	Association (A)
3. antenna	t.v. antenna, aerial	Acceptable Substitution (AS)
	electric pole, weather vane	Visual Substitution (VS)
	wires	Association (A)
	t.v. thing	Circumlocution (C) [Indefinite Noun (IN)]
	radar	Chained (CH)
4. statue	monument	Acceptable Substitution (AS)
	horse, rider, knight, warrior	Part/Whole (PW)
	picture	Coordinate (CO)
	sculpture	Superordinate (SUP)
	man on a horse, horse and a man on it	Circumlocution (C) [Visual Substitution (VS)]
	historic	Functional Attribute (FA)
5. crutch	crutches	Acceptable Substitution (AS)
	helper	Functional Attribute (FA)
	cane stick	Circumlocution (C) [Coordinate (CO)]
	walking cane	Circumlocution (C) [Functional Attribute (FA) Coordinate (CO)]
	walking stick	Circumlocution (C) [Functional Attribute (FA)]
	cane	Coordinate (CO)
	clutch	Phonemic Attribute (PA)

C Table C-1 (continued) Suggested Classifications of Typical Target-Word Substitutions on the TAWF—Section 1, Picture Naming: Nouns

Target Word	Substitution	Classification
6. suspenders	braces	Acceptable Substitution (AS)
	straps, bands	Visual Substitution (VS)
	man	Part/Whole (PW)
7. calculator	computer	Coordinate (CO)
	adding machine	Functional Attribute (FA)
	numbers	Part/Whole (PW)
	calendar	Phonemic Attribute (PA)
	digital	Association (A)
8. palm	palm of hand	Acceptable Substitution (AS)
	hand, arm	Locative Attribute (LA)
9. microphone	mike	Acceptable Substitution (AS)
	speaker	Coordinate (CO)
	gear shift	Visual Misperception* (VP)
	shaver, bulb	Visual Substitution (VS)
10. dice	die	Acceptable Substitution (AS)
	cubes, blocks	Visual Substitution (VS)
	dominoes	Coordinate (CO)
	black dots, spots	Part/Whole (PW)
	numbers	Association (A)
	dots on the dice	Circumlocution (C) [Part/Whole (PW)]
11. chopsticks	Chinese sticks	Circumlocution (C) [Association (A)]
	Japanese, Chinese	Association (A)
	toothpicks	Phonemic Attribute (PA)
	sticks	Visual Substitution (VS)
	chop	Phonemic Attribute (PA)
	pencils	Visual Misperception* (VP)
	bowl	Part/Whole (PW)
	tongs	Functional Attribute (FA)
	nutcracker	Visual Substitution (VS)
12. battery	small battery	Acceptable Substitution (AS)
	dynamite, box, tank	Visual Substitution (VS)
	radio	Locative Attribute (LA)
	garbage can, gas can	Visual Misperception* (VP)
13. eyebrow	eyelash, eyelid	Coordinate (CO)
	brow, eye	Phonemic Attribute (PA)
	lid	Locative Attribute (LA)
	red	Association (A)
14. binoculars	field glasses	Acceptable Substitution (AS)
	goggles, telescope, microscope	Coordinate (CO)
	eyeglasses	Superordinate (SUP)
	magnifying glass	Coordinate (CO)

*These target-word substitutions are not considered errors.

C **Table C-1** (continued) Suggested Classifications of Typical Target-Word Substitutions on the TAWF—Section 1, Picture Naming: Nouns

Target Word	Substitution	Classification
15. dart	arrow, spear	Visual Substitution (VS)
	dice	Phonemic Attribute (PA)
	umbrella, ice pick, stylus	Visual Misperception* (VP)
16. magnet	horseshoe, "U", shoe	Visual Substitution (VS)
	shoehorn	Chained (CH)
	magnetic	Functional Attribute (FA)
	magnifying	Phonemic Attribute (PA)
17. acorn	mushroom, corn, pear	Visual Substitution (VS)
	walnut, chestnut, hickory nut	Coordinate (CO)
	nut	Superordinate (SUP)
	squirrel nut	Circumlocution (C) [Association (A)]
	pine, fruit, banana	Chained (CH)
18. igloo	ice house	Circumlocution (C) [Superordinate (SUP) Compositional Attribute (COM)]
	Eskimo house, Eskimo hut	Circumlocution (C) [Functional Attribute (FA)]
	cave	Visual Substitution (VS)
	home, house, building	Superordinate (SUP)
	iceberg	Association (A)
	canoe	Phonemic Attribute (PA)
	tunnel, doorway, hallway	Part/Whole (PW)
	cabin, shed, hut	Coordinate (CO)
	doghouse	Visual Misperception* (VP)
19. starfish	star	Visual Substitution (VS)
	sea star	Circumlocution (C) [Locative Attribute (LA) Visual Substitution (VS)]
	fish	Superordinate (SUP)
	shellfish	Phonemic Attribute (PA)
	sea fish	Circumlocution (C) [Superordinate (SUP) Locative Attribute (LA)]
	star flower	Circumlocution (C) [Visual Substitution (VS)]
	shell, sand dollar, anemone, seashell, seaweed	Association (A)
	catfish, lobster, jellyfish	Coordinate (CO)

*These target-word substitutions are not considered errors.

C **Table C-1** (continued)
Suggested Classifications of Typical Target-Word Substitutions on the TAWF—Section 1, Picture Naming: Nouns

Target Word	Substitution	Classification
20. film	filmstrip	Acceptable Substitution (AS)
	pictures	Functional Attribute (FA)
	wheel, tape, thread, belt	Visual Substitution (VS)
	stamps	Visual Misperception* (VP)
	slide	Subordinate (SUB)
	movie screen	Coordinate (CO)
21. backpack	knapsack	Acceptable Substitution (AS)
	back	Locative Attribute (LA)
	camping bag, school bag	Functional Attribute (FA)
	camera bag	Visual Substitution (VS)
	book bag	Visual Substitution (VS) Functional Attribute (FA)
	back sack, back satchel	Phonemic Attribute (PA)
	knit bag, tote bag, suitcase, case, handbag, satchel, luggage, duffel bag	Coordinate (CO)
	pack	Superordinate (SUP)
	bag	Coordinate (CO)
	sack carrier	Circumlocution (C) [Functional Attribute (FA)]
	bookcase, book	Association (A)
22. unicorn	horse	Superordinate (SUP)
	hair, horn, mane, ear	Part/Whole (PW)
	Capricorn, caprican	Phonemic Attribute (PA)
	mares	Subordinate (SUB)
	horn horse	Circumlocution (C) [Superordinate (SUP) Part/Whole (PW)]
23. harmonica	mouth organ	Acceptable Substitution (AS)
	music	Functional Attribute (FA)
	french harp, mouth harp	Circumlocution (C) [Coordinate (CO)]
	violin, flute, horn, whistle, xylophone	Coordinate (CO)
	harp, harpsichord, monica	Phonemic Attribute (PA)
	bus	Visual Misperception* (VP)
24. wishbone	pulley bone	Acceptable Substitution (AS)
	lucky, food	Association (A)
	chicken	Locative Attribute (LA)
	chicken bone	Superordinate (SUP)
	fish bone	Phonemic Attribute (PA)
	plate	Part/Whole (PW)
	tongs	Visual Substitution (VS)

*These target-word substitutions are not considered errors.

C Table C-1 (continued) Suggested Classifications of Typical Target-Word Substitutions on the TAWF—Section 1, Picture Naming: Nouns

Target Word	Substitution	Classification
	bone	Superordinate (SUP)
	drumstick, thigh	Coordinate (CO)
25. propeller	popular, propilator	Phonemic Attribute (PA)
	helicopter, airplane	Locative Attribute (LA)
	wings, galley	Coordinate (CO)
	airplane wings	Circumlocution (C) [Coordinate (CO)]
	fan	Visual Substitution (VS)
	fender	Chained (CH)
	blades	Part/Whole (PW)
	airplane motor	Circumlocution (C) [Association (A)]
26. jack	car thing	Circumlocution (C) [Locative Attribute (LA) Indefinite Noun (IN)]
	lifter	Functional Attribute (FA)
	clamp	Part/Whole (PW)
	wrench	Coordinate (CO)
	tire jack, monkey jack	Subordinate (SUB)
	tire tool	Circumlocution (C) [Functional Attribute (FA) Superordinate (SUP)]
27. thimble	thumb	Locative Attribute (LA)
	thorn, thistle	Phonemic Attribute (PA)
	thumb thing	Circumlocution (C) [Locative Attribute (LA) Indefinite Noun (IN)]
	thumbtack	Chained (CH)
	spool, spindle	Coordinate (CO)
	thread, needle	Part/Whole (PW)
	darn	Association (A)
	needle and thread	Circumlocution (C) [Part/Whole (PW)]
28. compass	clock, watch, barometer, weather vane	Coordinate (CO)
	gauge	Superordinate (SUP)
	rim	Part/Whole (PW)
	campus	Phonemic Attribute (PA)
	direction	Functional Attribute (FA)
	magnifying glass, stopwatch	Visual Substitution (VS)
	you tell directions with it	Circumlocution (C) [Functional Attribute (FA)]
29. funnel	oil holder	Circumlocution (C) [Functional Attribute (FA)]
	oil, gas, gas tank, sifter	Association (A)

C Table C-1 (continued)
Suggested Classifications of Typical Target-Word Substitutions on the TAWF—Section 1, Picture Naming: Nouns

Target Word	Substitution	Classification
	tunnel, fossil	Phonemic Attribute (PA)
	you put gas in it	Circumlocution (C) [Functional Attribute (FA)]
	tack, horn, light bulb	Visual Substitution (VS)
	siphon	Coordinate (CO)
	golf tee	Visual Misperception* (VP)
30. pliers	wrench, screwdriver	Coordinate (CO)
	wire pliers	Subordinate (SUB)
	tool	Superordinate (SUP)
	tweezers	Visual Substitution (VS)
	pincher	Functional Attribute (FA)
31. dustpan	trash picker upper, sweeping pan	Circumlocution (C) [Functional Attribute (FA)]
	dishpan, dustbin, bedpan, pan	Phonemic Attribute (PA)
	sweeper, dust mop	Association (A)
	house shovel	Circumlocution (C) [Locative Attribute (LA) Visual Substitution (VS)]
	shovel, tray, scoop, scooper	Visual Substitution (VS)
	dustless pan	Circumlocution (C) [Phonemic Attribute (PA)]
	trash can, wastebasket	Association (A)
32. hopscotch	hopscotch thing, hopscotch game	Acceptable Substitution (AS)
	game	Superordinate (SUP)
	hopcross, hipscotch	Phonemic Attribute (PA)
	numbers, block, lines, board	Part/Whole (PW)
	tick-tack-toe, puzzle	Coordinate (CO)
	outside	Locative Attribute (LA)
	shuffleboard	Visual Substitution (VS)
33. blimp	Goodyear Blimp, zeppelin, dirigible	Acceptable Substitution (AS)
	airship	Superordinate (SUP)
	balloon	Visual Substitution (VS)
	airplane, helicopter, spaceship	Coordinate (CO)
	submarine	Visual Substitution (VS)
	Goodyear, Hindenberg	Association (A)
	Goodyear car	Circumlocution (C) [Association (A)]
	air balloon, hot air balloon, air bubble	Circumlocution (C) [Visual Substitution (VS) Compositional Attribute (COM)]

*These target-word substitutions are not considered errors.

C **Table C-1** (continued)
Suggested Classifications of Typical Target-Word Substitutions on the TAWF—Section 1, Picture Naming: Nouns

Target Word	Substitution	Classification
34. thermos	lunch thermos, thermos jug, thermos bottle	Acceptable Substitution (AS)
	container	Superordinate (SUP)
	canteen, pitcher, canister, percolator, jug	Coordinate (CO)
	coffee pot, coffee maker, funnel	Association (A)
	coffee	Functional Attribute (FA)
	mug, cup	Part/Whole (PW)
	stein	Visual Substitution (VS)
	coffee cooler	Circumlocution (C) [Functional Attribute (FA)]
	furnace, thermostat	Phonemic Attribute (PA)
35. tambourine	drums, cymbals, banjo, bells	Coordinate (CO)
	tangine, tangerine	Phonemic Attribute (PA)
	jingle-jingle, boom-boom	Acoustic Attribute (AA)
	instrument	Superordinate (SUP)
	red part	Part/Whole (PW)
	band drums	Circumlocution (C) [Locative Attribute (LA) Coordinate (CO)]
	music	Functional Attribute (FA)
36. spatula	knife, spoon, scoop, ladle	Coordinate (CO)
	stirrer, mixer, whipper, scraper, beater	Functional Attribute (FA)
	something to stir with	Circumlocution (C) [Functional Attribute (FA)]
	batter, cake mix	Association (A)
	bowl	Part/Whole (PW)
	cake paddle	Circumlocution (C) [Association (A) Visual Substitution (VS)]
37. seahorse	horse fish, fish horse	Visual Substitution (VS) Superordinate (SUP)
	horse	Visual Substitution (VS)
	fish	Superordinate (SUP)
	starfish, swordfish, lizard, unicorn, snail, alligator, shellfish	Coordinate (CO)
	sea animal, sea fish	Circumlocution (C) [Superordinate (SUP) Locative Attribute (LA)]
	sea monster, sea scorpion	Circumlocution (C) [Locative Attribute (LA) Association (A)]
	shell	Association (A)
	sawhorse	Phonemic Attribute (PA)

C Table C-2
Suggested Classifications of Typical Target-Word Substitutions on the TAWF—Section 2, Sentence Completion Naming

Target Word	Substitution	Classification
1. saddle	strap, belt	Association (A)
	back	Locative Attribute (LA)
	seat	Superordinate (SUP)
2. lava	magma	Acceptable Substitution (AS)
	larva, stava	Phonemic Attribute (PA)
	coal	Visual Substitution (VS)
	erosion, eruption, rupture, tornado	Association (A)
	volcanic ash	Coordinate (CO)
3. badge	identification	Functional Attribute (FA)
	license	Coordinate (CO)
	ticket, gun, duty	Association (A)
4. microscope	telescope	Coordinate (CO)
	scope, stethoscope, tele	Phonemic Attribute (PA)
	magnifying glass	Coordinate (CO)
	tube	Visual Substitution (VS)
5. leash	collar	Coordinate (CO)
	chain, rope	Compositional Attribute (COM)
	belt, strap, shoe, harness	Association (A)
6. shelf	bookshelf	Acceptable Substitution (AS)
	card, table, file, list, ledger	Association (A)
	schedule	Part/Whole (PW)
	case, rack	Coordinate (CO)
	spot	Locative Attribute (LA)
	library	Repetition (R)
7. paw	tail, nose, leg, ears, foot, head, back, feet	Coordinate (CO)
	hair	Compositional Attribute (COM)
8. diploma	education report card, exam, test, grades, records	Association (A)
	degree	Superordinate (SUP)
	certificate	Coordinate (CO)
9. thorn	sticker	Functional Attribute (FA)
	petal, leaf needle	Coordinate (CO)
	plant	Locative Attribute (LA)
	nail, pin, spike, point	Visual Substitution (VS)
	splinter	Association (A)
	thumb	Locative Attribute (LA)
10. seed	row, farm, garden, bed	Locative Attribute (LA)
	tomato, fruit	Part/Whole (PW)
	plant, tree, crop, bulb	Coordinate (CO)
	food	Superordinate (SUP)

C Table C-2 (continued) Suggested Classifications of Typical Target-Word Substitutions on the TAWF—Section 2, Sentence Completion Naming

Target Word	Substitution	Classification
	vegetable garden, vegetable	Repetition (R)
	stuff	Unspecified Noun (UN)
	sow	Part/Whole (PW)
11. peak	summit, apex	Acceptable Substitution (AS)
	highest point, point	Repetition (R)
	tip-top	Locative Attribute (LA)
	tip, top, point	Coordinate (CO)
	pike	Association (A)
	mountain top	Circumlocution (C) Visual Substitution (VS)
12. globe	sphere, circle	Visual Substitution (VS)
	a round, round model	Repetition (R)
	moon, sun, planet, land	Association (A)
	equator, crust	Part/Whole (PW)
	atlas, map	Coordinate (CO)
	world	Association (A)
13. jockey	rider, racer	Functional Attribute (FA)
	race car driver	Circumlocution (C) [Functional Attribute (FA)]
	jock, hockey	Phonemic Attribute (PA)
	horse race, rodeo	Locative Attribute (LA)
14. telescope	scope	Phonemic Attribute (PA)
	micro, bino	Chained (CH)
	microscope, periscope	Coordinate (CO)
	binoculars, magnifying glass	Coordinate (CO)
15. lullaby	rock-a-bye	Subordinate (SUB)
	musical	Superordinate (SUP)
	baby song	Circumlocution (C) [Superordinate (SUP)]
	baby, crib, cradle, pacifier	Association (A)
	harmony, melody, psalm, song	Coordinate (CO)
	gentle song	Repetition (R)
	bedtime story, nighttime story	Circumlocution (C) [Part/Whole (PW)]
	nursery rhyme	Functional Attribute (FA)
16. aisle	walkway	Functional Attribute (FA)
	column	Visual Substitution (VS)
	hallway	Coordinate (CO)
	pew, row	Association (A)
	middle	Locative Attribute (LA)
	rows of seat, space	Repetition (R)
	furrow	Visual Substitution (VS)

C Table C-3
Suggested Classifications of Typical Target-Word Substitutions on the TAWF—Section 3, Description Naming

Target Word	Substitution	Classification
1. siren	alarm	Superordinate (SUP)
	signal	Functional Attribute (FA)
	warning, fire truck	Repetition (R)
	horn, lights, flashing lights	Coordinate (CO)
2. helmet	fiberglass, hard	Compositional Attribute (COM)
	cap, glove, hard hat	Coordinate (CO)
3. tattoo	blood, hypo, thread, x-ray, red	Part/Whole (PW)
4. escalator	elevator	Coordinate (CO)
	stairs	Repetition (R)
5. jury	jury duty	Association (A)
	judge, witness, defendant, lawyer, jurist	Coordinate (CO)
	court	Repetition (R)
	supreme	Association (A)
6. robot	android	Acceptable Substitution (AS)
	machine	Repetition (R)
	computer	Part/Whole (PW)
7. seed	bulb	Acceptable Substitution (AS)
	flower, vegetable	Repetition (R)
	nut	Visual Substitution (VS)
	stuff	Unspecified Noun (UN)
8. costume	clown suit	Subordinate (SUB)
	uniform, mask	Coordinate (CO)
	down suit	Chained (CH)
	suit	Superordinate (SUP)
	clown	Association (A)
	evening gown, formal wear, tuxedo	Part/Whole (PW)
	masquerade, disguise	Functional Attribute (FA)
9. equator	globe, hemisphere	Locative Attribute (LO)
	Prime Meridian, latitude, axis	Coordinate (CO)
	atmosphere, moon, ozone, sun, comet	Association (A)
	equal	Phonemic Attribute (PA)
	east/west, sphere	Part/Whole (PW)
	orbit	Coordinate (CO)
	circle	Repetition (R)
10. hamper	clothes hamper	Acceptable Substitution (AS)
	dirty clothes basket, clothes basket	Repetition (R)
	pamper, panther	Phonemic Attribute (PA)
	wastebasket, laundry basket	Coordinate (CO)
	tub, laundry	Association (A)

C Table C-3
Suggested Classifications of Typical Target-Word Substitutions on the TAWF—Section 3, Description Naming

Target Word	Substitution	Classification
11. bangs	hair, forehead	Repetition (R)
	crew cut, beard, mohawk punk, bob	Coordinate (CO)
	scalp, top	Locative Attribute (LA)
	bowls	Association (A)
12. oar	hoars	Phonemic Attribute (PA)
	sail, propeller, motor, anchor, rudder, paddle wheel	Coordinate (CO)
	rower	Functional Attribute (FA)
	stick	Visual Substitution (VS)
	paddle, a long paddle	Repetition (R)

C Table C-4
Suggested Classifications of Typical Target-Word Substitutions on the TAWF—Section 4, Picture Naming: Verbs

Target Word	Substitution	Classification
1. dancing	playing	Superordinate Verb (SUPV)
	fighting, boxing	Visual Misperception* (VP)
2. licking	tasting	Coordinate Verb (COV)
	drinking	Associated Verb (AV)
	eating	Superordinate Verb (SUPV)
	tongue	Picture Labeling (PL)
3. pulling	yanking, tugging	Coordinate Verb (COV)
	breaking, raking, picking	Associated Verb (AV)
	pull	Root-Word Verb* (RWV)
4. squeezing	lemon squeezing	Acceptable Substitution (AS)
	dripping	Part/Whole Verb (PWV)
	cleaning, spilling, dipping	Associated Verb (AV)
	squeeze	Root-Word Verb* (RWV)
5. dripping	drip	Root-Word Verb* (RWV)
	drop, water, faucet, leaky faucet	Picture Labeling (PL)
	running	Chained (CH)
	dipping, dropping	Phonemic Attribute Verb (PAV)
	leaking	Superordinate Verb (SUPV)
	watering, raining	Associated Verb (AV)
6. rolling	rolling dough	Acceptable Substitution (AS)
	cooking	Associated Verb (AV)
	kneading, baking	Coordinate Verb (COV)
	making	Pro-Verbal Action (PVA)
	dough	Picture Labeling (PL)
7. drilling	screwing, riveting, grinding, cutting	Coordinate Verb (COV)
	boring	Superordinate Verb (SUPV)
	holes	Related Noun (RN)

*These target-word substitutions are not considered errors.

C Table C-4 (continued) Suggested Classifications of Typical Target-Word Substitutions on the TAWF—Section 4, Picture Naming: Verbs

Target Word	Substitution	Classification
	screwdriving	Innovative Verb (IV)
	a drill	Picture Labeling (PL)
8. measuring	weighing	Subordinate Verb (SUBV)
	writing, drawing	Associated Verb (AV)
	ruling, heightening	Innovative Verb (IV)
	checking height	Circumlocution (CV) [Part/Whole Verb (PWV)]
9. marching	walking, walk	Superordinate Verb (SUPV)
	soldier, parade, band	Picture Labeling (PL)
10. braiding	plaiting	Acceptable Substitution (AS)
	breading, bretting	Phonemic Attribute Verb (PAV)
	knotting, weaving, tying	Coordinate Verb (COV)
	tying hair	Circumlocution (CV) [Associated Verb (AV)]
11. winking	blinking, squinting	Coordinate Verb (COV)
	face, eye	Picture Labeling (PL)
	oinking, wicking	Phonemic Attribute Verb (PAV)
	looking, smiling, crying	Associated Verb (AV)
12. plugging	unplugging	Acceptable Substitution (AS)
	putting in, inserting, putting, pulling, sticking	Pro-Verbal Action (PVA)
	switching	Associated Verb (AV)
	plug	Root-Word Verb* (RWV)
	connecting	Superordinate Verb (SUPV)
	current	Chained (CH)
	splicing	Coordinate Verb (COV)
13. filing	file	Root-Word Verb* (RWV)
	putting, pulling	Pro-Verbal Action (PVA)
	filling	Phonemic Attribute Verb (PAV)
	packing, stacking, mailing	Coordinate Verb (COV)
	storing	Superordinate Verb (SUPV)
	taking out, putting away	Part/Whole Verb (PWV)
	putting back in	Circumlocution (CV) [Part/Whole Verb (PWV)]
	researching	Associated Verb (AV)
	desk	Chained (CH)
14. weighing	scaling	Innovative Verb (IV)
	weighting	Phonemic Attribute Verb (PAV)
	standing, looking, watching	Part/Whole Verb (PWV) Associated Verb (AV)
	weight	Related Noun (RN)

*These target-word substitutions are not considered errors.

C Table C-4 (continued) Suggested Classifications of Typical Target-Word Substitutions on the TAWF—Section 4, Picture Naming: Verbs

Target Word	Substitution	Classification
15. grating	shredding	Acceptable Substitution (AS)
	squeezing, scraping, sifting, dicing, chopping, peeling, grinding, cutting	Coordinate Verb (COV)
	scrubbing	Visual Substitution Verb (VSV)
	scratching	Subordinate Verb (SUBV)
	grate	Root-Word Verb* (RWV)
	working	Pro-Verbal Action (PVA)
	peeling an onion	Circumlocution (CV) [Coordinate Verb (COV)]
	screaming	Chained (CH)
16. begging	holding, reaching, handing, standing	Part/Whole Verb (PWV)
	holding a hat, pulling off hat	Circumlocution (CV) [Part/Whole Verb (PWV)]
	asking, collecting	Coordinate Verb (COV)
	giving, offering	Visual Misperception* (VP)
	walking, loafing, bowing panhandling	Associated Verb (AV) Subordinate Verb (SUBV)
	hand out	Related Noun (RN)
	beggar	Picture Labeling (PL)
	bumming	Coordinate Verb (COV)
17. threading	yarn, needle, thread	Picture Labeling (PL)
	sewing	Superordinate (SUPV)
	needling	Innovative Verb (IV)
	knitting, stitching, tying	Associated Verb (AV)
	putting through a needle, pulling through	Circumlocution (CV) [Part/Whole Verb (PWV)]
	stitching a needle	Circumlocution (CV) [Associated Verb (AV)]
	inserting through	Circumlocution (CV) [Pro-Verbal Action (PVA)]
	putting	Pro-Verbal Action (PVA)
18. knitting	threading	Associated Verb (AV)
	sewing, weaving, cross-stitching, crochet, crocheting	Coordinate Verb (COV)
	making	Pro-Verbal Action (PVA)
	thread	Chained (CH)
19. parachuting	flying in the air	Circumlocution (CV) [Part/Whole Verb (PWV)]
	hanging, falling, floating, dropping	Part/Whole Verb (PWV)
	coasting, flying, jumping, sailing	Associated Verb (AV)

*These target-word substitutions are not considered errors.

C Table C-4 (continued)
Suggested Classifications of Typical Target-Word Substitutions on the TAWF—Section 4, Picture Naming: Verbs

Target Word	Substitution	Classification
	diving	Chained (CH)
	skydiving, ballooning	Coordinate Verb (COV)
	parachute	Root-Word Verb* (RWV)
20. directing	police officer, policeman, police	Picture Labeling (PL)
	giving directions, telling where to go	Circumlocution (CV) [Pro-Verbal Action (PVA)]
	direction of traffic	Related Noun (RN)
	guarding traffic	Circumlocution (CV) [Chained (CH)]
	stopping	Subordinate Verb (SUBV)
	crossing	Chained (CH)
	waving, motioning, blowing, whistling	Part/Whole Verb (PWV)
	policing, patrolling	Superordinate Verb (SUPV)
	operating, ordering, guiding, passing, showing, signaling	Pro-Verbal Action (PVA)
	trafficking	Innovative Verb (IV)
21. developing	processing, working, holding, making	Pro-Verbal Action (PVA)
	focusing, filming	Associated Verb (AV)
	delapping	Phonemic Attribute Verb (PAV)
	photographing	Superordinate Verb (SUPV)
	bringing out, dipping, dunking, washing, rinsing, wetting, watering, immersing	Part/Whole Verb (PWV)
	develop	Root-Word Verb* (RWV)
	photo, film	Picture Labeling (PL)

*These target-word substitutions are not considered errors.

C Table C-5
Suggested Classifications of Typical Target-Word Substitutions on the TAWF—Section 5, Category Naming

Target Word	Substitution	Classification
1. holidays	days off	Functional Attribute (FA)
	seasons	Association (A)
	months of the year	Circumlocution (C) [Association (A)]
2. states	countries, cities	Coordinate (CO)
	places	General Noun (GN)
3. time	time element, time of day	Acceptable Substitution (AS)
	week	Subordinate (SUB)
	hours, day	Repetition (R)
	clock	Association (A)
	measurement	Superordinate (SUP)

C **Table C-5** (continued)
Suggested Classifications of Typical Target-Word Substitutions on the TAWF—Section 5, Category Naming

Target Word	Substitution	Classification
4. presidents	people, persons	General Noun (GN)
	towns	Part/Whole (PW)
5. oceans	seas, rivers, lakes	Coordinate (CO)
	water	Compositional Attribute (COM)
	capitals, states	Association (A)
	people, nationality, railroad	Part/Whole (PW)
6. rivers	Mississippi	Repetition (R)
	lakes	Coordinate (CO)
	countries, states	Association (A)
	water	Compositional Attribute (COM)
	bodies, places	General Noun (GN)
7. planets	Pluto, Saturn	Subordinate (SUB)
	Mars, Earth, Jupiter	Repetition (R)
	space, universe, solar system	Locative Attribute (LA)
	stars, comets	Coordinate (CO)
	place where people live	Circumlocution (C) [Functional Attribute (FA)]
8. dances	dancing	Acceptable Substitution (AS)
	waltz	Repetition (R)
	actions, moves	Compositional Attribute (COM)
	movement	Superordinate (SUP)
	walk	Coordinate (CO)
	exercise	Functional Attribute (FA)
9. religions	faith, denominations	Acceptable Substitution (AS)
	what you believe in	Circumlocution (C) [Functional Attribute (FA)]
	worship	Functional Attribute (FA)
	church	Locative Attribute (LA)
	Christian, Baptist	Subordinate (SUB)
	Jewish	Repetition (R)
	culture	Coordinate (CO)
	priest, God's	Association (A)
10. seasons	months of the year	Circumlocution (C) Compositional Attribute (COM)
	times of the year	Circumlocution (C) [Superordinate (SUP)]
	fall	Subordinate (SUB)
	weather, climate, temperature, time zone	Association (A)
	months	Compositional Attribute (COM)
	days of the month	Circumlocution (C) [Association (A)]

C **Table C-5** (continued) Suggested Classifications of Typical Target-Word Substitutions on the TAWF—Section 5, Category Naming

Target Word	Substitution	Classification
11. silverware	utensils, flatware, cutlery, tableware	Acceptable Substitution (AS)
	eating tools, use to eat	Circumlocution (C) [Functional Attribute (FA)]
	kitchen	Locative Attribute (LA)
	dishes, plate	Coordinate (CO)
	place setting	Part/Whole (PW)
	eating	Functional Attribute (FA)
	devices	General Noun (GN)
	tools	Superordinate (SUP)
	food	Association (A)
12. directions	West	Subordinate (SUB)
	North	Repetition (R)
	places, part, sections, points	General Noun (GN)
	continents, poles, latitude	Association (A)
	like a compass	Circumlocution (C) [Functional Attribute (FA)]
13. countries	nations	Acceptable Substitution (AS)
	states, cities, capitals	Compositional Attribute (COM)
	places	General Noun (GN)
	continents	Superordinate (SUP)
	government	Association (A)
	Europe	Subordinate (SUB)
14. senses	hear, see	Subordinate (SUB)
	smell	Repetition (R)
	feelings	Subordinate (SUB)
	actions, reactions, functions	Association (A)
	things	Indefinite Noun (IN)
15. cities	towns, major city	Acceptable Substitution (AS)
	countries, states	Coordinate (CO) or Superordinate (SUP)
	places	General Noun (GN)
	crime spots	Circumlocution (C) [Association (A)]
	capital	Subordinate (SUB)
16. transportation	vehicles, conveyances	Acceptable Substitution (AS)
	travel means, get around	Circumlocution (C) [Functional Attribute (FA)]
	train traveling	Circumlocution (C) [Functional Attribute (FA) Subordinate (SUB)]
	traffic	Association (A)
	motor	Compositional Attribute (COM)

C **Table C-5** (continued)
Suggested Classifications of Typical Target-Word Substitutions on the TAWF—Section 5, Category Naming

Target Word	Substitution	Classification
	recreational, travel, rides	Functional Attribute (FA)
	cars, automobiles, locomotives	Subordinate (SUB)
17. metals	hard material	Circumlocution (C) [Compositional Attribute (COM)]
	steel, iron, copper	Repetition (R)
	parts	General Noun (GN)
	minerals, ore, element	Superordinate (SUP)
	industry	Association (A)
18. appliances	kitchen	Locative Attribute (LA)
	electric	Association (A)
	food openers	Part/Whole (PW)
	tools, equipment, machines	Superordinate (SUP)
	utensil	Coordinate (CO)
	supplies	General Noun (GN)
	things you do	Circumlocution (C) [Indefinite Noun (IN) Functional Attribute (FA)]
19. awards	things you won	Circumlocution (C) [Functional Attribute (FA)]
	rewards	Phonemic Attribute (PA)
	honor, honors	Functional Attribute (FA) Superordinate (SUP)
	iron, aluminum	Compositional Attribute (COM)
	statues, certificate	Subordinate (SUB)
	winning, winner	Association (A) or Functional Attribute (FA)
	trophies, medals, plaques	Repetition (R)
	gift, prizes, souvenirs	Coordinate (CO)
	commendations	Superordinate (SUP)
20. organs	human organs, internal organs	Acceptable Substitution (AS)
	parts of body, human body	Circumlocution (C) [Locative Attribute (LA)]
	parts	General Noun (GN)
	guts, bowels, intestine, lung	Subordinate (SUB)
	body	Locative Attribute (LA)
	stomach	Repetition (R)
	tissue, flesh	Compositional Attribute (COM)
	anatomy, system	Superordinate (SUP)
	parts of anatomy	Circumlocution (C) [Superordinate (SUP)]
21. punctuation	quotations, decimal	Subordinate (SUB)
	exclamation	Chained (CH)
	comma	Repetition (R)

C **Table C-5** (continued)
Suggested Classifications of Typical Target-Word Substitutions on the TAWF—Section 5, Category Naming

Target Word	Substitution	Classification
	English, grammar	Association (A)
	sentence, endings	Locative Attribute (LA)
	what you put after	Circumlocution (C) [Locative Attribute (LA)]
	symbol, sign, marks	Superordinate (SUP)
	abbreviations	Coordinate (CO)

APPENDIX D

Response Analysis of Substitution Types

D Figure D-1
Response analysis for Sections 1, 2, 3, and 5

Name ____________________

Grade ____________ Age ____________

Adolescent ____________ Adult ____________

Target Words for Section 1	Subject Response	SUP	CO	SUB	FA	LA	COM	A	CH	PA	IS	R	AA	VS	VP*	PW	IN	GN	UN	C	SC†	NR†
1. ruler																						
2. mask																						
3. antenna																						
4. statue																						
5. crutch																						
6. suspenders																						
7. calculator																						
8. palm																						
9. microphone																						
10. dice																						
11. chopsticks																						
12. battery																						
13. eyebrow																						
14. binoculars																						
15. dart																						
16. magnet																						
17. acorn																						
18. igloo																						
19. starfish																						

*Not considered an error on the TAWF.
†SC = self-correction; NR = no response.

D Figure D-1 (continued)
Response analysis for
Sections 1, 2, 3, and 5

Name ____________________

Grade ____________ Age ____________

Adolescent ____________ Adult ____________

Target Words for Section 1	Subject Response	SUP	CO	SUB	FA	LA	COM	A	CH	PA	IS	R	AA	VS	VP*	PW	IN	GN	UN	C	SC†	NR†
20. film																						
21. backpack																						
22. unicorn																						
23. harmonica																						
24. wishbone																						
25. propeller																						
26. jack																						
27. thimble																						
28. compass																						
29. funnel																						
30. pliers																						
31. dustpan																						
32. hopscotch																						
33. blimp																						
34. thermos																						
35. tambourine																						
36. spatula																						
37. seahorse																						

*Not considered an error on the TAWF.
†SC = self-correction; NR = no response.

D Figure D-1 (continued)
Response analysis for
Sections 1, 2, 3, and 5

Name ______

Grade ______ Age ______

Adolescent ______ Adult ______

Target Words for Section 2	Subject Response	SUP	CO	SUB	FA	LA	COM	A	CH	PA	IS	R	AA	VS	VP*	PW	IN	GN	UN	C	SC†	NR†
1. saddle																						
2. lava																						
3. badge																						
4. microscope																						
5. leash																						
6. shelf																						
7. paw																						
8. diploma																						
9. thorn																						
10. seed																						
11. peak																						
12. globe																						
13. jockey																						
14. telescope																						
15. lullaby																						
16. aisle																						

*Not considered an error on the TAWF.
†SC = self-correction; NR = no response.

D Figure D-1 (continued)
Response analysis for
Sections 1, 2, 3, and 5.

Name ____________________

Grade ____________ Age ____________

Adolescent ____________ Adult ____________

Target Words for Section 3	Subject Response	SUP	CO	SUB	FA	LA	COM	A	CH	PA	IS	R	AA	VS	VP*	PW	IN	GN	UN	C	SC†	NR†
1. siren																						
2. helmet																						
3. tattoo																						
4. escalator																						
5. jury																						
6. robot																						
7. seed																						
8. costume																						
9. equator																						
10. hamper																						
11. bangs																						
12. oar																						

*Not considered an error on the TAWF.
†SC = self-correction; NR = no response.

D **Figure D-1** (continued)
Response analysis for
Sections 1, 2, 3, and 5.

Name ____________________

Grade ____________ Age ____________

Adolescent ____________ Adult ____________

Target Words for Section 5	Subject Response	SUP	CO	SUB	FA	LA	COM	A	CH	PA	IS	R	AA	VS	VP*	PW	IN	GN	UN	C	SC†	NR†
1. holidays																						
2. states																						
3. time																						
4. presidents																						
5. oceans																						
6. rivers																						
7. planets																						
8. dances																						
9. religions																						
10. seasons																						
11. silverware																						
12. directions																						
13. countries																						
14. senses																						
15. cities																						
16. transportation																						
17. metals																						
18. appliances																						
19. awards																						
20. organs																						
21. punctuation																						

*Not considered an error on the TAWF.
†SC = self-correction; NR = no response.

D Figure D-2

Response Analysis for Section 4.

Name ______________________________

Grade ______________ Age ______________

Adolescent ______________ Adult ______________

Target Words for Section 4	Subject Response	SUPV	COV	SUBV	PVA	RN	AV	CH	PAV	ISV	RWV*	VSV	VP*	PWV	PL	IV	CV	SC†	NR†
1. dancing																			
2. licking																			
3. pulling																			
4. squeezing																			
5. dripping																			
6. rolling																			
7. drilling																			
8. measuring																			
9. marching																			
10. braiding																			
11. winking																			
12. plugging																			
13. filing																			
14. weighing																			
15. grating																			
16. begging																			
17. threading																			
18. knitting																			
19. parachuting																			
20. directing																			
21. developing																			

*Not considered an error on the TAWF.
†SC = self-correction; NR = no response.

APPENDIX E

Mean TAWF Raw Scores and Standard Deviations of Subjects in the Standardization Sample

E Table E–1

		TAWF Section										TAWF Total*	
		1		2		3		4		5			
Grade	***N***	***Mean***	***SD***	***Mean***	***SD***	***Mean***	***SD***	***Mean***	***SD***	***Mean***	***SD***	***Mean***	***SD***
7	200	30.81	3.5	13.51	1.9	9.81	1.7	16.61	2.4	17.92	2.3	88.64	8.86
8	200	31.16	3.5	13.94	1.6	10.19	1.4	16.98	2.2	18.06	2.4	90.32	8.18
9	200	32.03	3.6	14.35	1.6	10.56	1.3	17.44	2.2	18.64	2.1	93.01	8.15
10	200	32.04	3.2	14.63	1.4	10.49	1.3	17.60	2.2	18.74	2.1	93.50	7.20
11	200	32.43	3.3	14.57	1.3	10.47	1.5	17.77	1.9	19.08	1.7	94.32	6.98
12	200	32.97	3.1	14.77	1.4	10.81	1.1	18.27	2.1	19.43	1.6	96.23	6.68
Age (in years-months)													
20–0 to 39–11	201	34.42	2.4	15.20	1.1	11.16	1.0	19.10	1.6	19.54	1.7	99.43	5.97
40–0 to 59–11	200	32.81	3.5	15.03	1.2	11.02	1.2	19.30	1.6	19.24	1.9	97.38	7.04
60–0 to 80–0	152	29.40	4.8	14.56	1.5	10.19	1.5	18.34	1.9	18.15	2.3	90.65	9.60

*Means of Total score may not equal sum of Section means because of rounding.

APPENDIX F

Grade- and Age-Level Standards for TAWF Time Measurements

F-1 **Table F-1**
Grade- and Age-Level Standards for TAWF Estimated Item Response Time (ERT), Based on Number of Response Delays (4 Seconds or Longer) Produced by Less than 20% of the Normal Subjects in the Standardization Sample

	GLS (Number of Response Delays—4 Seconds or Longer)	
Grade	**TAWF Complete Test**	**TAWF Brief Test**
7	5 or more	2 or more
8	5 or more	2 or more
9	4 or more	2 or more
10	4 or more	2 or more
11	4 or more	2 or more
12	4 or more	2 or more
Age (in years-months)		
12–0 to 12–11	5 or more	2 or more
13–0 to 13–11	5 or more	2 or more
14–0 to 14–11	4 or more	2 or more
15–0 to 15–11	4 or more	2 or more
16–0 to 16–11	4 or more	2 or more
17–0 to 19–11	4 or more	2 or more
20–0 to 39–11	3 or more	2 or more
40–0 to 59–11	4 or more	2 or more
60–0 to 80–0	7 or more	3 or more

F-2 Table F-2
Grade- and Age-Level Standards and Upper and Lower Bounds of GLS Confidence Range for TAWF Average Item Response Time, Based on Means and Standard Deviations by Grade or Age of the Normal Subjects in the Standardization Sample

Grade	Average Item Response Time (in seconds)	
7	Grade-Level Standard (GLS)	2.33
	Upper Bound of GLS	2.60
	Lower Bound of GLS	2.06
	Mean	1.72
	SD	0.61
8	GLS	2.22
	Upper Bound of GLS	2.48
	Lower Bound of GLS	1.96
	Mean	1.63
	SD	0.59
9	GLS	2.06
	Upper Bound of GLS	2.28
	Lower Bound of GLS	1.84
	Mean	1.55
	SD	0.51
10	GLS	2.11
	Upper Bound of GLS	2.35
	Lower Bound of GLS	1.87
	Mean	1.57
	SD	0.54
11	GLS	1.99
	Upper Bound of GLS	2.20
	Lower Bound of GLS	1.78
	Mean	1.50
	SD	0.49
12	GLS	2.00
	Upper Bound of GLS	2.23
	Lower Bound of GLS	1.77
	Mean	1.47
	SD	0.53
Age (in years-months)		
20–0 to 39–11	GLS	2.10
	Upper Bound of GLS	2.48
	Lower Bound of GLS	1.72
	Mean	1.39
	SD	0.71
40–0 to 59–11	GLS	2.25
	Upper Bound of GLS	2.55
	Lower Bound of GLS	1.95
	Mean	1.68
	SD	0.57
60–0 to 80–0	GLS	2.98
	Upper Bound of GLS	3.44
	Lower Bound of GLS	2.52
	Mean	2.11
	SD	0.87

APPENDIX G

Prorated Accuracy Scores for Percent of Known Words Named Correctly

G Table G-1

Percent of Known Words Named Accurately	Prorated Accuracy Raw Score Complete TAWF	Prorated Accuracy Raw Score TAWF Brief Test	Percent of Known Words Named Accurately	Prorated Accuracy Raw Score Complete TAWF	Prorated Accuracy Raw Score TAWF Brief Test
1	1	0	51	55	20
2	2	1	52	56	21
3	3	1	53	57	21
4	4	2	54	58	22
5	5	2	55	59	22
6	6	2	56	60	22
7	7	3	57	61	23
8	9	3	58	62	23
9	10	4	59	63	24
10	11	4	60	64	24
11	12	4	61	65	24
12	13	5	62	66	25
13	14	5	63	67	25
14	15	6	64	68	26
15	16	6	65	70	26
16	17	6	66	71	26
17	18	7	67	72	27
18	19	7	68	73	27
19	20	8	69	74	28
20	21	8	70	75	28
21	22	8	71	76	28
22	24	9	72	77	29
23	25	9	73	78	29
24	26	10	74	79	30
25	27	10	75	80	30
26	28	10	76	81	30
27	29	11	77	82	31
28	30	11	78	83	31
29	31	12	79	85	32
30	32	12	80	86	32
31	33	12	81	87	32
32	34	13	82	88	33
33	35	13	83	89	33
34	36	14	84	90	34
35	37	14	85	91	34
36	39	14	86	92	34
37	40	15	87	93	35
38	41	15	88	94	35
39	42	16	89	95	36
40	43	16	90	96	36
41	44	16	91	97	36
42	45	17	92	98	37
43	46	17	93	100	37
44	47	18	94	101	38
45	48	18	95	102	38

G Table G-1 (continued)

Percent of Known Words Named Accurately	Prorated Accuracy Raw Score Complete TAWF	Prorated Accuracy Raw Score TAWF Brief Test	Percent of Known Words Named Accurately	Prorated Accuracy Raw Score Complete TAWF	Prorated Accuracy Raw Score TAWF Brief Test
46	49	18	96	103	38
47	50	19	97	104	39
48	51	19	98	105	39
49	52	20	99	106	40
50	54	20	100	107	40